OUR FELLOW IMMIGRANTS

Also by Robert Froman

QUACKO AND THE ELPS
WANTED: AMATEUR SCIENTISTS
THE NERVE OF SOME ANIMALS
MAN AND THE GRASSES

OUR
FELLOW
IMMIGRANTS

by ROBERT FROMAN

illustrated by Anne Marie Jauss

DAVID McKAY COMPANY, INC.   NEW YORK

OUR FELLOW IMMIGRANTS

COPYRIGHT © 1965 BY ROBERT FROMAN

LIBRARY OF CONGRESS CATALOG CARD NUMBER: 65-16914

MANUFACTURED IN THE UNITED STATES OF AMERICA

VAN REES PRESS • NEW YORK

Typography by Charles M. Todd

To the memory of
Harry Hunter Froman

ACKNOWLEDGMENTS

A BOOK like this requires the help of specialists in many different fields. I especially want to thank Charles Elton of Oxford University; Edgar Anderson of the Missouri Botanical Garden; Wayne D. Rasmussen of the U.S. Department of Agriculture; Willis King and Gardiner Bump of the U.S. Fish and Wildlife Service; Tom L. McKnight of the University of California at Los Angeles; George Gaylord Simpson of Harvard University; Alexander Langmuir of the U.S. Public Health Service; Donald A. Dukelow of the Division of Environmental Medicine, American Medical Association; Roland C. Clement of the National Audubon Society; John C. Pallister and Richard G. Van Gelder of the American Museum of Natural History; Clarence Cottam of the Welder Wildlife Foundation; and Elsie M. Knight of the Sharlot Hall Historical Museum, Prescott, Arizona.

I also want to thank the editors of *American Heritage* magazine for permission to use some of the material from my article, "Our Fellow Immigrants," which first appeared in that publication.

R.F.

CONTENTS

INTRODUCTION

Our human species, *Homo sapiens*, is only one among many kinds of living things that have immigrated to the New World and prospered greatly. Horses and cows, cats and mice, chickens and carp, wheat and cabbage—the list is long and varied.

These fellow immigrants of ours come from many different parts of the Old World. Horses are from Central Asia. Chickens are from the jungles of southeastern Asia. Cats are from East Africa. Carp are from Europe. Wheat is from Western Asia.

Most had human help in getting here and establishing themselves. The earliest Spanish, English and French settlers brought along their cows and pigs and goats and sheep and chickens and grains and vegetables and other domestic animals and plants to start new herds and crops in the New

World. Today, the descendants of these cows, for instance, outnumber by more than a million to one their nearest native relatives, the bison.

Some newcomers were brought by men for human purposes but were then able to strike out on their own. The wild horses of the western plains are among the best examples of this. Thousands of them still roam wild and free in remote desert areas.

Many other species were brought here by men, then turned loose to see if they could fend for themselves. Only a few could, but some of those have done spectacularly well. Chinese pheasants, Hungarian partridges and English sparrows are examples of such success. An even greater success has been achieved by one of the least loved of all our birds —the starling.

Certain of our immigrants that came here with human help were not given that help knowingly. They were unwanted hitchhikers, most vigorously discouraged whenever noticed. This did not bother such species as German cockroaches and Norway rats. They refused to be discouraged, found that they like it here and are doing very well indeed.

These two and most other species to be discussed emigrated from the Old World into both the southern and northern parts of the New. A few others have come into this country from South or Central America. The animals among them, such as the nutria and chinchilla, are of minor importance, but such plants as corn, potatoes and tomatoes are among our major crops.

Finally, a distinction should be made between the few species that arrived here under their own power and those that had human help. It can be argued that only the former are entitled to be called immigrants and that the others should be called "introductions" because they did not come of their own free will. This is little more than quibbling, though, and raises such questions as what to call the millions of human immigrants who came here as children, slaves, indentured servants or otherwise as a result of someone else's decision.

Anyway, whether called immigrants or introductions, each newcomer species has behind it a story, sometimes a story that goes back many millions of years.

SIBERIA   ALASKA

CHAPTER ONE

East Meets West

FOR THE first several hundred million years of life on
earth living creatures had nothing to do with dry land.
Life originated in the sea and stayed there until about three
hundred and fifty million years ago. At that time the most
highly developed animals were the fishes. They had become
so varied and numerous and so intensely competitive with
each other for living space in the sea that several kinds had
adapted to the shallow waters of the sea's edge.

One aid to such adaptation was a primitive sort of lung
which permitted the possessor to take oxygen directly from
the air in addition to extracting it from the water with its
gills in the good old fishy way. Eventually, some of the owners of this new-fangled equipment climbed out of the water
and began spending most of their time on dry land. These
were the early representatives of the great class of the
Amphibia whose descendants today, the frogs and toads and

such, still usually spend their early days in water or, anyway, in very moist places.

As the years passed, millions by millions, the amphibians spread to many parts of the dry land and produced several widely varied branches. One branch acquired the ability to do without the watery start, and from it evolved the reptiles who soon replaced amphibians as lords of the land. A few million years later a branch of the reptiles gave rise in turn to the earliest representatives of our own class, the mammals.

During all this animal evolving, the continents were changing, too. Sometimes the sea encroached and separated them with wide stretches of water. At other times the sea receded and left them linked together in one great, more or less continuous land mass.

Toward the end of the Age of Reptiles, the Mesozoic Era, which drew to a close some sixty million years ago, the continents were closely connected with each other. Many of the great species of dinosaurs were distributed over much of the earth. In the following Cenozoic Era, our own Age of Mammals, some of the continents sometimes have been separated from each other.

One of the more tenuous links has been that between Alaska and Siberia. During part of the Cenozoic Era a land bridge connected them and made possible occasional interchanges of species that developed in the eastern and western hemispheres. The horse and camel families, for instance, did much of their evolving in the western hemisphere and spread via the land bridge to the eastern. The mastodon, mammoth, bison and others reversed this process.

But many kinds of mammals long remained peculiar to one hemisphere or the other. Paleontologists feel sure that representatives of our own family of mammals, the *Hominidae,* did not arrive here until late in the family's evolution.

A century of digging for fossils throughout this hemisphere has turned up no bones or other evidence of any apes or ape-men. The nearest such that preceded us here are our far distant cousins, the flat-nosed monkeys of South America, which are among the more primitive members of our order, the Primates.

Asia and Africa are rich in representatives of this order—chimpanzees, gorillas, orangutans, gibbons and many species of monkeys, baboons, lemurs, lorises and others. Those continents also have yielded fossils of even closer relatives of ours, including extinct members of our family and even of our genus. *Homo erectus,* or Java man, is among the best known of the latter. But none of these relatives seems to have made it across the Siberia-to-Alaska land bridge.

By 50,000 B.C., however, members of our own species, *Homo sapiens,* were becoming comparatively numerous and spreading from their probable place of origin in Africa throughout the eastern hemisphere. At that time the last Ice Age was near its height. Much of the world's water supply was locked in the glaciers, and the oceans' level thus was so lowered that the Siberia-to-Alaska land bridge may have been a thousand or more miles in width. Despite its far northern latitude, the bridge itself may have been ice free because, paradoxically, the nearby Arctic Ocean then was comparatively warm. In any case, primitive Siberian hunters would have been able to make their way across it and almost certainly did so.

Just when the first Siberian crossed probably never will be known. It may have been some thousands of years after 50,000 B.C. or some thousands earlier. When the glaciers began melting away about 10,000 B.C., they covered those early immigrants' tracks with a hundred feet of sediment, plus several hundred feet of water, and turned the bridge into the present, fifty-six-mile-wide Bering Strait.

Long before then the Siberian hunters—probably group after group over thousands of years—had pushed their way far to the South. By 1492 A.D. when the first representatives of the next great wave of immigrants arrived and mistook the Siberians' descendants for natives of India, those misnamed "Indians" populated the hemisphere from the Arctic to Cape Horn.

It is an old and arrogant habit of the descendants of the new immigrants from Europe to take it for granted that their forefathers conquered the descendants of the old immigrants from Siberia. This is only partly true. All across the northern reaches of Alaska and Canada, in the jungles of Central America and the Amazon basin and in several other areas live descendants of the old immigrants to whom word that they had been conquered would be news, indeed. Also, in many countries of Central and South America descendants of the old immigrants far outnumber descendants of the new. Even in this country millions of citizens have old immigrants among their ancestors.

The whole story of human immigration to this hemisphere is a long, resounding contradiction of Rudyard Kipling's famous dictum, "Oh, East is East, and West is West, and never the twain shall meet." For one thing, our "Westerners" came here from lands to the east of us, and they include besides Europeans the hundreds of thousands of African immigrants who began arriving in Columbus's time. Similarly, our "Easterners" in Kipling's sense arrived here from the west. They include, in addition to the Siberians, sizeable numbers from the Philippines, China, Japan and India.

In this hemisphere East and West mean the opposite from what they meant to Kipling, and they not only have met but also have blended inextricably.

CHAPTER TWO

Fellow Immigrant #1

T HE EARLIEST human immigrants from Siberia probably brought with them little more than the clothes they wore and the hunting weapons they carried, but later groups almost certainly crossed the land bridge to Alaska with company—four-footed company. It is possible that that company followed at a little distance and of its own accord. More likely, the humans considered the company a valuable possession and insisted on its going along.

The probable company was the dog (*Canis familiaris*), the first domesticated animal. That many Indian tribes owned domesticated dogs before Columbus's voyage of discovery is certain. In fact, the Incas of Peru had several different breeds resembling modern sheepdogs, dachshunds and bulldogs, and it had taken many generations of breeding to develop them. The reason for the slight uncertainty about whether the ancestors of these dogs immigrated from Siberia with men is that it is just barely possible the Indians developed their dogs by taming one or another of the several kinds of wolves they found here before them.

Underlying this uncertainty is another, broader one. Paleontologists and zoologists have not yet been able to decide from which species of wolves (*Canis lupus*), jackals (*Canis aureus* and *Canis lupaster*) and other dog-like animals the modern dog is descended. There are many kinds of still-living animals scattered around Europe, Asia and North America which may be the dog's ancestor, and some extinct species are possibilities, too. Most are so closely related that they can interbreed, so several could be jointly ancestral to the dog.

Some experts think the question of how dogs came to be domesticated is easier to answer. Stone Age men, wolves and jackals all hunted and ate the same kinds of game animals. Both wolves and jackals are glad to eat carrion when it is available. It must have happened again and again that groups of them would get into the habit of hanging around human camps to pick up unwanted game entrails and other refuse. From permitting the animals to eat refuse to offering them food or even adopting and feeding puppies would have been an easy step.

At first the sole purpose of keeping the puppies may have been to provide amusement. Even today primitive people have been observed adopting and keeping young animals as pets with no thought of getting any material advantage from them. Students of the prehistoric period theorize that, since wolves are pack animals used to following a leader, puppies so adopted could easily have given their allegiance to human leaders. This would have made them valuable assistants in hunting when they grew up, and as soon as men discovered this, they would have gone in for dog raising in a steady way.

The trouble with this nice, neat explanation is that it is all too pat. Among the Indian tribes of California, for instance, anthropologists found four quite different kinds of relationships between humans and dogs. Some tribes fitted the theory closely and valued dogs chiefly for their usefulness in hunting deer. Other tribes kept dogs only for eating. Others barely tolerated dogs and grudgingly let them cadge occasional scraps. Others considered dogs rare and wonderful creatures to be kept only as pets, pampered and carried around in their owner's arms. One or all of these attitudes, or another quite different one, may have prevailed among the Stone Age men who first took up with dogs.

Whatever the truth may be, it seems certain that men domesticated dogs long before any other animals. The process probably began in the Old World a good deal more than 15,000 years ago. This was long before the melting of the glaciers of the last Ice Age submerged the Siberia-to-Alaska land bridge and makes it quite possible that some of the human immigrants from Siberia brought along, or were voluntarily accompanied by, canine ones.

By the time of Columbus and the subsequent new wave of immigration, thousands of years of breeding had produced many kinds of dogs in the Old World. In Spain one of the most favored and most numerous breeds was a kind of greyhound, and it is possible that such Spanish greyhounds were the first post-Columbus canine immigrants to the new world.

So many were brought here and produced so many puppies that some early writers about American animals thought greyhounds were a native American breed.

Since then, of course, thousands of dogs of scores of breeds have come here, and the greyhound long since has become a minor type. In colonial and pioneer times the more popular breeds were working dogs that could make themselves useful helping to herd sheep and cattle or tracking and retrieving game animals. The overwhelming majority of American dogs probably always have been of no particular breed, however.

Today, interest in purebred dogs seems to be growing as a result of the spread of affluence and the quest for status. According to pet food manufacturers, Americans now spend something like $400,000,000 a year on prepared dog foods; and according to the American Kennel Club, which registers purebred animals, the poodle is the most popular breed as of this writing. It comes in three sizes and is considered one of the basic breeds because it has been traced back to first-century Roman times.

Second and third in popularity are the German shepherd and the beagle, but anyone who wants to use a dog to help him climb socially or in his own esteem is likely to turn to one of the newer and more exotic types. There now are well over a hundred recognized breeds in this country, nearly all of them immigrant. Good examples of some of the further reaches for the unusual are two African breeds fairly new here. One is the Basenji of the Congo, a small dog notable chiefly because it does not bark. The other is the Rhodesian ridgeback or lion dog, a big one with a ridge down the middle of its back.

More interesting to naturalists than any of these is the

result of an increasing number of crosses of immigrant dogs with one of our native wolves. By the 1920's timber wolves were exterminated in this country except for a few small enclaves along our northern border. One of the results of this extermination has been a great expansion in the range of the coyote or prairie wolf (*Canis latrans*). Coyotes used to range only from the Great Plains westward because they could not compete in other areas with the bigger and stronger timber wolves. Now coyotes range from coast to coast and each year turn up in new areas.

In the environs of Los Angeles, in upstate New York and in some other places coyotes are interbreeding with dogs. The results of these crosses are sometimes called coydogs. Resembling the coyote parent much more than the dog, these are unmistakably wild animals. So far, only a few have been observed, but it is just possible that a new and distinctly American type of wild dog is in the making.

CHAPTER THREE

Unhorsed Continent Rehorsed

I N SOME circles it is considered important to be able to trace one's family tree a century or two into the past. A few British, Roman, Chinese and other aristocrats feel, and are considered by some of their fellow countrymen, ineffably superior because they can trace their ancestors back a thousand years or so. By such standards horses (*Equus caballus*) can well look down their noses at all humans. The horse family tree can be traced easily and clearly almost all the way back to the dawn of the Cenozoic era, some seventy or more million years ago.

One might quibble about this on the grounds that the horse's seventy-million-year-old ancestor was far different from its modern descendant, but the fact remains that both ancestor and descendant are members of the same family, the *Equidae.* Our own human family, the *Hominidae,* which includes besides our species, *Homo sapiens,* a few others like Neanderthal man, appears to be not much more than a couple of million years old.

Throughout most of its multimillion-year history, the horse family seems to have been exclusively American. The little "dawn horse," Eohippus, one of the family's earliest members, left fossil remains scattered around both the eastern and western hemispheres, but most of the many species of horses that have evolved, flourished for a while and finally become extinct since his day left remains that have been found only in the New World. Eohippus was less than a foot high at the shoulder, weighed under a hundred pounds and had four toes on each front foot and three on each hind one. One of the most detailed of all fossil records of evolution is that of the family's slow increase in size and abandonment of all but one toe per foot.

Over the geologic ages after the extinction of Eohippus in the Old World, a few other species of New World horses spread back to Asia via the Bering Strait land bridge, but until one or two million years ago none of these migrant species succeeded in establishing itself there for very long. While these late emigrants prospered, however, the stay-at-homes slowly languished. The last native American horse apparently died at least a few thousand years ago.

This extinction puzzled Charles Darwin. In his *On the Origin of Species* he pointed out that the gradual disappearance of the American horse, or any other kind of animal or plant, could have resulted from environmental conditions extremely difficult to detect. A slight change in that environment, however, might make it highly favorable to the animal or plant in question.

A change much in favor of horses began to take place in the western hemisphere upon the arrival of Columbus. The change was caused by the almost unanimous preference of Europeans for riding a horse rather than eating it. Inhabitants of the Old World had begun to acquire this preference some four thousand years before Columbus's voyage of discovery, at about the time that American Indians may have been tipping the scales decisively against waning native horse herds by hunting them for food. The paradoxical fact is that what made possible the sensational biological success of the wild horse in America after Columbus was the domestication of the horse in Europe and Asia.

Archeologists are not in full agreement yet about the when, where and by whom of the first horse domestication, but the general outlines of the story are fairly clear. It almost certainly was not the work of one of the more advanced peoples of Egypt or the Near East. They seem to have learned it from barbarians from the steppes north of the Black Sea. These may have learned their horsemanship from others further east in what is now Turkestan, who probably accomplished the first taming by 2,500 B.C. or a few centuries earlier.

In any case, by 1493 A.D., horses were by far the most important means of land transportation throughout much of the Old World and so highly valued that only in remote desert areas were a scattered few able to escape capture. On returning to Spain in March of that year with news of his discovery, Columbus immediately set about preparing for his second voyage, to leave that September. Among the many things he assembled to take along were twenty of the best horses in Spain. At a parade in Seville the magnificent animals assigned to him by the government made an impressive sight.

Along with the horses, however, he had been assigned cavalry officers to ride them. Just before the expedition left Cadiz these officers sold the expensive horses, substituted the cheapest nags they could find and pocketed the difference. Since the cheap nags probably were better fitted to survive the long, hard voyage, this was premonitory of one of the chief developments in the horse family on its return to America.

Not until three centuries later did that development become noticeable, though. On later voyages Spanish colonists succeeded in transporting horses more imposing by human standards and in establishing on Cuba and other Caribbean islands big horse-breeding centers. When it turned out that many Indians were terrified by the sight of a man on horseback, mistaking this apparition for a single, monstrous animal, all Spanish explorers made it a point to take along cavalry. In 1519 Hernando Cortez sailed from Cuba for the Mexican coast with a force of only six hundred men, ten cannon and sixteen horses and proceeded to obliterate the Aztec empire. Many factors contributed to the Conquistador's success against enormous odds, but the horses undoubtedly were among his most important advantages. Twelve years later Francisco Pizarro needed only one hundred foot soldiers to supplement the sixty-two horsemen he led to Peru to begin his conquest of the Incas.

For several decades the Spanish colonists took care to see that the people they conquered and enslaved did not get too well acquainted with the beasts which so impressed them. It was against Spanish law for an Indian to own or even to ride a horse. But by the end of the first century after the conquest of Mexico, colonists had pushed north up the Rio Grande into New Mexico. They were then so far from centers of authority that it was easy to ignore the law and much more convenient to make cowboys out of the local Indians than to import help all the way from Spain.

Eventually, this seemingly reasonable bit of scofflaw activity proved a bad mistake, at least from the Spanish point of view. In 1680 the New Mexican Indians rose against their oppressors and either killed or drove out all the Spaniards, keeping the horses. Partly through trade and partly through thievery, these horses and their descendants, together with others stolen from the Spaniards, spread north among the tribes of the Great Plains, the mountains and the deserts with almost explosive speed.

One result was that, although the Spanish were able to reconquer the New Mexican tribes in 1696, they made little further progress northward. Horses transformed tribes like the Apaches and Comanches from comparatively feeble primitives into some of the most effective warriors, man-for-man, the world ever has known. By the early eighteenth century, horses and horsemanship had spread all the way from Mexico through the western half of the continent into what is now Canada, and many tribes began preparing for their heroic hundred years' war against the invaders from Europe.

But the more spectacular result of spreading Spanish horses through the West was biological. There is no record of when the first horses strayed from Spanish or Indian herds into the wilds and managed to survive and raise colts. It used to be thought that such early sixteenth-century explorers as De Soto and Coronado might have started the wild herds, but historians who have looked closely at the evidence consider this highly unlikely. Not until after 1700 did travelers in the southern Plains country begin to mention seeing occasional wild horses. Yet by the middle of the nineteenth century some of the greatest herds of wild horses the world has known roamed over those Plains.

As a young lieutenant, Ulysses S. Grant rode through Texas on his way to take part in the Mexican War of 1846.

"A few days out from Corpus Christi," he wrote later, "the immense herd of wild horses that ranged at that time between the Nueces and the Rio Grande was seen directly in advance of the head of the column and but a few miles off. The column halted for a rest and a number of officers, myself among them, rode out two or three miles to see the extent of the herd.

"The country was a rolling prairie, and from the higher ground the vision was obstructed only by the earth's curvature. As far as the eye could reach to our right, the herd extended. To the left, it extended equally. There was no estimating the animals in it; I have no idea that they could all have been corralled in the State of Rhode Island, or Delaware, at one time. If they had been, they would have been so thick that the pasturage would have given out the first day."

Recently, Professor Tom L. McKnight of the Department of Geography, University of California at Los Angeles, has made an attempt to do what Grant thought impossible. After studying all available evidence, McKnight estimates that the total of wild horses in the West at their nineteenth-century peak was probably between two million and five million. The greatest concentrations were in Texas, but Oklahoma, New Mexico and Colorado also had huge herds. (The technically correct term for such horses, incidentally, is not "wild" but "feral," because they are descended from domesticated animals.)

It was among these horses that there took place the development foreshadowed by the unprepossessing nature of the first modern horses in the New World, the ones brought by Columbus on his second voyage. As every Western fan knows, a wild horse is called a mustang. Less well known is that the name is an anglicized form of a Spanish word meaning simply a stray animal and that most mustangs are allowed to stray only because they are of little or no use for human purposes.

This contradicts the basic premise of countless wild-horse stories, but it is an obvious fact to anyone who encounters modern mustangs in Idaho, Nevada or other western states where several thousand still range. Most are small to the point of runtiness; they have misshapen heads, sway-backs, knobby legs and other features that horrify those who consider themselves "good judges of horseflesh." Now and then a more valuable-looking animal turns up in the wild; a century or so ago this happened somewhat oftener. In those days horses in general were far more valuable than now and the forage available to wild ones considerably richer, so that a few expert and extremely hard-working mustangers could make a living by capturing, training and selling wild horses. Today, almost the only thing they can be sold for is dog food.

But all this is in terms of human values. In terms of fitness to survive on their own, mustangs are far superior to most horses brought to this hemisphere by Europeans. The latter were the result of several thousand years of selective breeding for human purposes and often ill equipped to live without human care. A huge work-horse of the Percheron breed or a racing Thoroughbred would have trouble staying alive on its own for even a few days in wild-horse country. The small size of the mustangs and their other inelegant features are precisely what fit them for life in the wild.

Like the herds of native buffalo, the wild-horse herds of the Great Plains stood in the way of civilization. Their imminent extinction was beginning to be announced regularly even before young Lieutenant Grant saw that huge parade of them. It still is re-announced every once in a while. Someday it may actually take place if the human population continues to explode until it covers every square foot of land, but that day still seems a bit in the future. The mustangs have been pushed out of the grasslands into the remotest mountains and deserts and occasionally are pursued in those places by airborne mustangers, but the numbers of the animals actually may be on the increase. They continue to receive new additions from the herds on farms and ranches where machines each year supplant more animals.

A few romanticists like to believe that this means the modern wild horses no longer are "pure" mustangs. They argue that the original mustangs were of Spanish breeds and the modern recruits to the wild herds are of breeds brought here from other parts of the Old World. Since all domesticated horses are of the same species and, left to their own devices in the wild, tend to produce offspring that become smaller and scrawnier as the generations pass, this makes little sense.

The more important of the breeds brought here since the first Spanish horses were the Percheron from France, Belgian from Belgium and the Shire, Clydesdale, Hackney, Thoroughbred and Shetland from Great Britain. A few others, such as the Morgan, Standard Bred and American Saddle horse, were developed here. More than nine out of ten American horses, however, always have been what breeders call "grades," meaning of no particular breed though distinctly a domesticated horse and not a reversion to the type of the wild ancestor.

Today, the domesticated horse is on the wane throughout the world. In this country its numbers fell from a high of over twenty-five million in 1915 to barely three million in 1959 when the U.S. Department of Agriculture stopped bothering with annual counts. And the wild horses of Asia from which the domestic descended have almost completely disappeared—"almost" because of a remote possibility that a few dozen of a type called Przewalski's horse may survive in Outer Mongolia.

The horse's cousin, the donkey or ass (*Equus asinus*), a native of Africa, also is on the wane, though it did not have as far downhill to go. Probably the first in this hemisphere were a few brought to Mexico in 1591, progenitors of that country's famous little burros. In this country two gifts to George Washington popularized the chief use for the species here. The King of Spain and the Marquis de Lafayette each presented to Washington a jack, as the male donkey usually is called, prized for its mule offspring, a mule being a cross between a jack and a horse. The powerful, patient mules sired by these jacks soon became famous around Mt. Vernon, and a number of other Virginia farmers took up breeding mules.

About 1800 Henry Clay and some fellow Kentuckians imported several jacks and established their state as the nation's mule-breeding center. By 1850, when Missouri took over that distinction, mules were the chief source of animal power in much of the South, and their importance kept growing, up to the time of World War I. Since then, of course, they have lost out to machines, though some Southern sharecoppers still depend on them.

Burros used by prospectors and others in the southwestern desert also have been replaced by such machines as jeeps. Turned loose like many farm horses, some burros have succeeded in establishing themselves on their own in remote parts of Nevada and California. Because the few other living members of the horse family—the never-domesticated zebras (*Equus zebra* and others) of Africa and onagers (*Equus hemionus*) of Asia—are rapidly being killed off or squeezed into zoos and parks, our bands of wild horses and burros soon may make the western hemisphere once more the home of the only members of the family capable of surviving on their own.

CHAPTER FOUR

Longhorns, Shorthorns
and No Horns

U NLIKE the horse family, all members of which are no-
ticeably horsey, the cattle family, called *Bovidae*, includes a great variety of animals—not only cows but also
goats, sheep, antelopes, bison, musk oxen, yaks and several
others. And cattle make themselves far more useful than
horses. In the Western world they supply beef, veal, milk,
butter, cheese, leather, hormones, vitamin extracts, bone
meal and fertilizer. In many parts of the world they also
supply much of the power for plowing, hauling, and milling
flour.

So valuable have cattle been, indeed, that our word for
them is closely involved with many of our words for wealth.

Chattel is one. Capital is another. And this is not a mere oddity of the English language. In Latin, for instance, the word for cattle was *pecus*. From this the Romans got their word for money, *pecunia*, and we in turn got our word pecuniary.

What is behind all this is the bovine family's ancient habit of eating and running, a habit necessary to a wild cow's survival. When members of the family living in the wild state find good pasturage of tall, thick grass, they cannot simply fall to and gorge to repletion. They have to grab as much as they can in a hurry, keep a sharp eye for wolves, lions or other carnivores likely to be creeping up toward them in the cover and take off fast at the first sign that one such is getting close. This is hard on the digestion if you have only a single, ordinary stomach. Cattle have four stomachs. In the wild, they stuff the first one full without bothering to chew, then regurgitate and chew the contents later when they find an open place where no carnivore can creep up on them. As a result, they have acquired the ability to digest the roughest sort of plant matter. From the human point of view, they turn indigestible raw cellulose into milk, meat and power.

Their potential for the latter probably was what most interested the late Stone Age men who first domesticated them. Until the harnessing of steam, cattle provided man his chief source of power other than his own muscles (horses big and strong enough for anything more than riding or charioteering were comparatively recent developments). But this does not mean that some cave man decided he needed an animal to help pull heavy loads and immediately set about breaking a wild cow to harness. Although no one is certain when, where and how cattle first were domesticated, the process must have been slow and roundabout.

In all likelihood that process began somewhere in southern Asia about eight to ten thousand years ago not long after
men had learned to grow crops of grain and other plants
and, as we shall see in the next chapter, to tame goats and
sheep. The farmers doubtless hunted wild cows for meat,
and the cattle probably returned the compliment by breaking into the cultivated fields in their own hunt for food. Anthropologists think the cattle-taming process may have begun
with the capture of a few calves and that, when someone
had the bright idea of tying a load on the back of one of
these beasts, its value soared.

Whatever it was that first persuaded those early farmers
of the value of tame cattle, the conviction soon found plenty
of backing. In some places other values outranked even
power, milk and meat. For men who fought each other with
spears and arrows, for instance, cattle hides revolutionized
warfare by providing light, tough shields. In areas where
wood was scarce, cattle dung made good fuel for cooking
fires. And like the modern Masai tribe of Kenya and Tangan-
yika, many early cattlemen got much of their nourishment
from blood drawn a little at a time from the veins of their
cows. For all these reasons the use of cattle spread throughout Asia, Europe and North Africa, and the wild animals became too valuable to leave that way. The rare few wild
herds that persisted into modern times in remote parts of
central Europe finally disappeared some three hundred
years ago.

Long before then, domestication had begun making great
changes in the animals. Early cattlemen knew nothing about
genetics, but they naturally concentrated on the more trac-
table animals; in fact, they probably had no way of holding
one really determined to break loose. Also, if they wanted

work, they kept the ones that worked best; if they wanted milk, they kept the ones that gave the most of it; and so on. By the time of Columbus, there were dozens of different breeds of domesticated cattle.

Along with the unprepossessing horses he took to Hispaniola on his second voyage, the great explorer also shipped a bull and several heifers of tough, strong Spanish stock which had been accustomed to semi-desert conditions for many generations. Twenty-eight years later, two years after Cortez began the conquest of Mexico, the first descendants of these cattle were taken to the mainland. The breed and the country were so well suited to each other that within half a century the baronial ranches of central and northern Mexico numbered their cattle in the tens of thousands.

By the early 1700's Mexican cattlemen were beginning to establish ranches north of the Rio Grande. In the two centuries since their arrival in this hemisphere the Mexican method of raising cattle by letting them run wild most of the time had made them even stronger and hardier; some developed huge, wide-spreading horns. These horns caught the imaginations of nearly all travelers in the area. By the middle of the nineteenth century the cattle were known throughout most of the English-speaking world as Texas longhorns and had begun to acquire almost as large and noisy a corps of volunteer press agents as the one that created the mustang legends.

The ballyhoo men had a lot to work with. Many longhorns were huge and powerful and had inexhaustible vitality. There were stories, some of them almost certainly true, of hunters pouring a dozen or more rifle shots into a wild longhorn cow without being able to stop her. And there were other stories of enraged longhorn bulls charging whole regiments of soldiers and scattering them like chaff.

It also is true that the profits to be made from longhorns were among the chief attractions that lured settlers from the United States to Texas when the latter still was Mexican soil. It even can be maintained with some reason that the longhorns created the cowboy. Men who tended cows were called cowherds until the 1830's when young Texans, out to stock their ranches, took up raiding Mexican longhorn herds. No one is sure who first called the raiders cowboys, but the intention was not flattering. The word indicated contempt for their violence and thievery, and that is what it continued to connote for many years until it was taken over by the dime novelists and Hollywood scenarists.

Despite the legends and the more solidly impressive aspects of the longhorns, they were a small, blind alley off the main thoroughfare of development of cattle in this country. The few that survive are mere curiosities. Western movies have so conditioned us to think of cattle raising as a business for wide-open spaces that it comes as a surprise to learn that nearly all our important breeds of cattle originated in the British Isles. What's more, British cattle were arriving and thriving in Virginia in 1611, three-quarters of a century before establishment of the first Mexican ranches in Texas.

The first British cattle had landed in Virginia in 1607 but were killed and eaten during a famine. The Virginia Company, which controlled the colony under a grant from King James I, shipped over more of the animals in 1611 and made it a dire offense for colonists to harm them in any way. Within ten years the colony had several hundred head, and within twenty years it was seeking markets for its surplus in Massachusetts and Connecticut. The New Englanders were not far behind in importing and raising cattle, however. One of the earliest established professions there was that of cow-herd, a most unromantic type who worked on foot and whose chief responsibility was to keep his charges out of the planted fields. He was an indispensable functionary in a time when every village had a herd of cows and little time or material for building cow-proof fences.

The small, scrawny seventeenth-century British cattle breeds were a long way from those of today, though. Not until a century later did the British begin to pioneer the scientific cattle breeding which produced the modern types. Lacking scientific criteria for choosing among available cattle, some colonists made up criteria of their own.

One of the most persistent of these was a strong prefer-ence for black cattle over red. The reasoning behind it was that black cattle must be strange and perhaps even inedible looking to the native wolves because these were used to preying on reddish deer. Actually, no wolf would pay any at-tention to the evidence of his eyes if his nose told him some-thing different, so the argument for black cattle was non-sensical. That did not prevent belief in it. Some families who pushed westward generation by generation carried this su-perstition intact and invulnerable all the way across the continent.

By the end of the eighteenth century the success of the British breeding experiments was clear to progressive Ameri-can farmers, and the build-up of herds of modern breeds of cattle got under way in this country. At first this was mostly the doing of gentlemen farmers like George Washington. Auction sales of pedigreed British cattle were important so-cial events in New York, Philadelphia and Baltimore, and a good deal of status went with owning blue-blooded bulls.

But the new types eventually proved so much more profit-able that only the most firmly stuck-in-the-mud farmers could resist them.

The first modern British breed widely adopted here was the Shorthorn, which produces both good milk-cows and good beef-steers. Since then most breeds have been devel-oped to specialize in one or the other. Jerseys and Guernseys from the Channel Islands are great producers of rich milk. One non-British breed, the Holstein-Friesian (usually called Holsteins) from Holland, produces milk in greater quantity but with less cream. The two chief beef-breeds are the white-faced Hereford and the hornless black Aberdeen Angus, now usually called Angus or Black Angus.

Although the latter is the latest important immigrant breed here, its origins lie so far back they never have been traced. For several centuries cattlemen on the northeast coast of Scotland have been raising hornless animals which they called humblies or doddies because of the lack of horns. These contemptuous terms, together with the romantic rep-utation of the Texas longhorns, apparently made many of the rest of the world's cattle breeders blind to the virtues of the Scottish breed. Anyway, until 1878 it was almost un-known outside Scotland. At the world's fair in Paris that year fifteen Black Angus from Scotland took nearly all the prizes over more than two thousand cattle of other breeds from around the globe. Shortly after that the Scottish cattle began arriving in this country in large numbers and climbing steadily in popularity.

Several other breeds of both milk and beef producing types are raised here, but the six mentioned above long have been dominant in this country except for the Gulf Coast area. There the heat and flies and ticks make it impossible for any European cattle to thrive for long. Early in this century, cattlemen in that area began trying an entirely new immigrant species, the humped zebu of India and Africa. Formally known as *Bos indicus* (the formal name of European cattle is *Bos taurus*) the zebu evolved in the tropics and takes heat, flies and such for granted. Crosses of several different types of zebu have produced the Brahman cattle, and a cross of this type with the Shorthorn has produced the new Santa Gertrudis breed, which already is producing much good beef in the Gulf States and is proving a boon in other similar parts of the world.

Today, this country's cattle far outnumber the combined total of all other farm livestock immigrants—horses, hogs, sheep and goats. There are more than a hundred million beef and milk cattle compared with fewer than sixty million hogs, twenty-eight million sheep and three million horses. In dollar value cattle are even more dominant, being worth about $14 billion compared with about $2 billion for all the others combined.

Perhaps the best indication of the high esteem cows have earned here is U.S. Patent No. 3,140,543 taken out in July, 1964, by a Colorado rancher. His invention is a bovine dental plate. Now no American cow ever again need worry about that toothless look.

CHAPTER FIVE

The Farmyard's Other
Hoofed Animals

ESPITE the current great importance of cattle and the high rank of horses until this century, two of the other three species of domesticated livestock—sheep (*Ovis aries*) and goats (*Capra hircus*)—preceded them in domestication. The third species—pigs (*Sus scrofa*)—probably were domesticated at about the same stage in civilization's development as cattle. Today, of course, pork is second only to beef in our national diet, and lamb and wool give sheep considerable value. But goats are little more than curiosities to most modern Americans.

It was not always this way. Goats were more valuable than sheep even as recently as in New England's pioneer

days. In some arid parts of the world they still are the favored animals because of their ability to thrive on plants
that cattle, sheep and pigs cannot digest. But their great role
in human affairs lies far in the past—to be as precise as possible, more than 10,000 years in the past.

By 9000 B.C. many of the inhabitants of the Near Eastern
hills surrounding the great Mesopotamian plain were settled
in permanent villages and had learned to grow grain and
other crops. For meat they still hunted the plentiful and
varied game-animals of the area with the help of their dogs,
the only animals they had yet learned to keep. During the
next thousand or so years, they took a big step, possibly
because of a phenomenon called "imprinting." This is the
tendency of certain kinds of new-born animals to follow the
first living things they see and hear as soon as they are able
to walk.

The Austrian zoologist, Konrad Lorenz, and several other
researchers have studied this behavior in great detail, and
many hunters have noticed it, too. In a recent issue of one
of the magazines for men who like to hunt and gossip about
their experiences, a writer told of encountering in the wilds
of British Columbia a moose that had just given birth to a
calf. In an attempt to decoy the man, the cow moose ran off
limping as if hurt. The man thought to get away and let the
mother return to her offspring, but when he tried to do so,
the calf staggered after him on wobbly legs, bleating piti-
fully. Several times he returned it to the spot where he had
found it, and each time he tried to leave, it followed him
again. In the end, he found that the only way to escape was
by running away at top speed.

Archeologists and anthropologists think that incidents of
such imprinting resulted in the domestication of the first

farm animals (as distinct from dogs, which were hunting companions and allies). They feel fairly sure that those first farm animals were goats. And they strongly suspect that the first ones were kept not for their milk or meat or hides but simply as pets.

This is an unsettling idea for Marxists and other materialists who like to believe that all great historic advances were motivated by the desire for material gain. The evidence for the theory is strong, however. Much the same kind of accidental pet-acquiring and pet-keeping behavior has been observed today among primitive tribes, and many a backwoods family in this country has adopted—or has been adopted by —motherless young deer.

From the bones found on the sites of several early Near Eastern villages archeologists also have deduced that sheep soon followed goats into domestication (or may even have been domesticated simultaneously). By 6000 B.C. considerable numbers of both species had been so long under human protection and control that even their fossilized bones are unmistakably different from those of their wild ancestors. They changed in other ways, too, of course. Goats eventually came to be esteemed for their milk, and since those that gave more milk were kept longer and treated better, they had more young. As a result, domesticated goats soon were giving much more milk than did the wild ones. In the early days sheep developed principally in the direction of providing more and more fat. Even today, mutton fat is highly valued in the Near East and many other parts of the world. To early sheep-keepers it probably was a great and glorious luxury.

The reason why that early craving for fat did not first lead to domestication of pigs, which produce it even more lav-

ishly than sheep, is that wild pigs are powerful and dangerous animals. A wild boar may weigh more than three
hundred pounds, stand as high as a Great Dane and run
faster. Protruding upward from its lower jaw are tusks several inches long with which it can disembowel a man in a
single raking thrust. To hunt such an animal even with a
high-powered rifle is far more dangerous than most kinds
of modern hunting, because a boar sometimes can absorb
several bullets and keep going. To hunt it with spears and
arrows was to take a great risk.

Yet countless thousands of primitive men did hunt wild
pigs. And after they had learned from their experience with
goats and sheep about raising animals for food, many different villages and tribes probably tried keeping and raising
captured young pigs. By five or six thousand years ago success was commonplace in areas of the Old World all the way
from China to Switzerland, and the pig keepers' natural
preference for gentler animals gradually made the domesticated breed more manageable.

Of these three animals only the sheep have close relatives
native to this hemisphere. The bighorn sheep (*Ovis cana-
densis* and others) of the Northwest are of the same genus
as domesticated sheep. Rocky Mountain goats (*Oreamnos
montanus*) actually are goat-antelopes, a different family
from the domesticated goat's, and the so-called wild pig of
the Southwest, the javelina or peccary (*Tagassu tajacu*), is
only distantly related to true pigs.

Yet pigs proved better adapted to the New World than
either sheep or goats. Columbus took several of each on his
second voyage. The goats and sheep did fairly well under
human care, but the pigs thrived both in pens and on their
own whenever and wherever they were able to break loose.

Within a few decades they were plentiful on most of the islands of the Caribbean. Within a century or so they reached the mainland and soon were running loose in what are now the Carolinas and Georgia.

The pigs brought here later by colonists from England also found the land much to their liking and tended to run a bit wild. One early visitor, an Englishman named Richard Parkinson, wrote a book entitled *A Tour in America in 1798, 1799, and 1800.*

"They," said Parkinson of American pigs, "are long in the leg, narrow on the back, short in the body, flat on the sides ... in make more like the fish called a perch than anything I can describe. You may as well think of stopping a crow as those hogs. They will go to a distance from a fence, take a run, and leap through the rails three or four feet above the ground, turning themselves sidewise in mid-air. They will suffer hardships as no other animal could endure."

These half-wild pigs, usually called woods hogs, were just about ideal for the purposes of families pioneering the country between the Appalachians and the Great Plains in the first half of the last century. The animals would walk alongside or under the wagon until the homesteader picked his site, feed themselves on whatever was available while he cleared the land and stand off nearly all predators with a yearning for pork. And when the land was well tamed, the pigs were quite content to settle down in pens and grow fat.

Some pigs made careers for themselves in the cities, too. Until after the Civil War the collection and removal of garbage from homes and restaurants was not considered, in many parts of the country, a proper function for municipal governments or any other human agencies. It was a job for pigs. In cities ranging in size from New York on down, the animals were permitted to roam the streets at will as the best and cheapest means of getting rid of refuse. Until it was realized that there could be a connection between filth and such diseases as cholera and typhoid fever, this practice was not even much protested, except when the pigs occasionally grew so bold as to attack children.

Once it came to be accepted that the best place for a pig was in a pen on a farm, a search for better breeds began. As in the case of cattle, Great Britain was the chief source of immigrant breeds, most of which bore the names of English shires—Berkshires, Hampshires, Yorkshires and Herefords. The only other important early breeds were developed in this country, including the Poland China, which was given its exotic name to impress farmers. Finally, in the 1930's the long, lean Landrace breed reached here from Denmark and started a trend away from excessive lardiness.

Both in their early history here and in the sources of their modern breeds, goats and sheep have been far different from pigs. By the time they reached the New World, they were much too far gone in dependence on man to revert to the wild state anywhere on the mainland. Panthers and wolves in the early days, and coyotes and dogs more lately, have made short work of any wandering goats and sheep. There is, however, one part of the country which lacks large predators. In 1778 the English explorer of the South Pacific, Captain James Cook, turned several goats loose in Hawaii. Fifteen years later another explorer, George Vancouver, contributed a number of sheep. Today, several of the islands still have sizeable herds of wild sheep and goats.

Until 1800 sheep raised on farms on the mainland did not differ much from those allowed to run loose in Hawaii. In 1801 an immigrant Frenchman named Eleuthère Irénée Du Pont de Nemours decided to start a gunpowder factory in Delaware and returned to France in search of equipment and technicians. Along with these, he brought back a ram named Don Pedro, a prize example of the Spanish Merino breed, which grew unusually fine and plentiful wool. With the help of some expert press agentry by M. Du Pont, Don Pedro and the offspring he sired soon became famous among American sheepmen and started a craze which led to importing thousands of other Merinos and the first attempts in this country to breed sheep scientifically. Merinos still are a widely favored breed of sheep here, though they have been joined by other immigrant breeds, chiefly from Great Britain, such as the blackfaced Shropshires and Suffolks.

The reason New Englanders valued sheep far less than goats in colonial days was that the latter gave more and better milk and were hardier. When cows became numerous and productive enough to supply all the milk needed, the goat and sheep ranking was reversed, and our twenty-eight million sheep now outnumber our goats by more than five to one. If only milch goats are considered, the disparity would be even greater. These, many of which are of the Toggenberg and Saanen breeds brought here from Switzerland since the turn of the century, number only a few tens of thousands, too few for the U.S. Department of Agriculture to bother keeping track of.

A nineteenth-century Turkish sultan was responsible for our only goat immigrants of much importance today. In 1849 the United States government sent to Turkey at the sultan's request a cotton expert to help set up some cotton-growing experiments in that country. The sultan was pleased with the expert's work and, on his departure, made him a present of nine Angora goats. These launched the United States mohair growing industry, now carried on chiefly in Texas which has about four million of these long-haired goats.

CHAPTER SIX

Cowhands vs. *Camels*

O NE MAY afternoon in 1856 a horseman riding southeast from San Antonio, Texas, toward the coast noticed in the distance what he took to be a train of pack mules. A little later his horse stiffened, sniffed the breeze that blew from the direction of the train, emitted a terrified whinny, threw the rider in the dust and bolted back whence he had come. When the train drew a little closer, the bewildered horseman was, for a moment, strongly inclined to follow his horse.

Out of the approaching cloud of dust loomed the improbable shapes of the U.S. Army's newest and most bizarre recruits, just landed on the Texas coast from the Turkish port of Smyrna. They were the thirty-four mounts of the Army's

First Camel Corps. The reaction of the traveler and his horse, described in his report by one of the officers accompanying the camels (*Camelus dromedarius*), foreshadowed the reception that was to be given the corps all the way across the Southwest from San Antonio to Los Angeles. It also foreshadowed the ultimate fate of what might have been a highly successful experiment.

That experiment had first been proposed twenty years earlier by Major George H. Crossman, one of the Army's early explorers of the West. It was a rather obvious and quite reasonable proposal. Since camels were so useful for transportation purposes in the desert countries of the Old World, said Crossman, they ought to be given a try in the American Southwest. As usual with new ideas, no matter how reasonable, this one took a while to bear fruit, but in 1855 the Army obtained from Congress $30,000 for the purpose of bringing in camels. A ship was sent to the Near East, and the animals were landed on the Texas coast the following year.

In one way, the idea was even better than Crossman or anyone else could know at that time. Paleontologists have discovered since then that the camel family, like the horse family, did nearly all its evolving in the Western Hemisphere. Four of the family's six species still are exclusively American —the llama, alpaca, guanaco and vicuña of the Andes. Another much like the modern camel still lived in what is now California as recently as 15,000 years ago. Not until about a million years ago did representatives of the family make their way over the land bridge from Alaska to Siberia, spread slowly across Asia and develop into the other two closely related modern species—the two-humped Bactrian camels of central and eastern Asia and the one-humped dromedaries, or Arabian camels, of western Asia.

As in the case of the horse, there now seems to be no way of determining exactly why camels died out in North America, but it is quite obvious why camels could not make the kind of comeback horses made when they re-immigrated. The bar was the animals' effect on the cowhands and teamsters assigned to handle them. Hollywood prettification of the Old West has been in nothing more absurd than in giving the impression that cowhands generally were kind to animals. They were the opposite.

One of the few writers of popular novels about the West who knew this well at firsthand was Owen Wister, author of *The Virginian.* Wister, who was a friend of Theodore Roosevelt, happened to show the President-to-be the first draft of a novel that included an incident in which an enraged cowhand gouged out the eyes of a horse. Roosevelt wrote a letter begging him to delete the incident not because it was unrealistic but because it might "encourage cruelty to animals."

From the point of view of many cowhands the trouble with the camels was that they would not submit to cruelty and had highly effective means of retaliating when it was inflicted on them. If, in the process of loading a camel, a man kicked it or struck it with a quirt as he might a mule, the camel would turn and spit in his face a big, evil-smelling wad of cud. Nothing, of course, could have been better calculated to enrage most cowhands. If they pushed the camel harder, they risked being badly torn by its tusklike incisor teeth of which it could make good use in self-defense.

This sort of thing, together with the terror camels usually inspired in horses encountering them for the first time, would have ended the Army's camel experiment in a hurry had it not been for young Lieutenant Edward F. Beale, one of the most colorful figures in the Southwest's early history. In 1846,

Beale and the frontier scout, Kit Carson, saved U.S. Army forces besieged near San Diego, California, by crawling through the Mexican army lines to fetch help. A few years later, Beale carried the first gold samples and news of the great discovery at Sutter's Mill in California across the continent to Washington, D.C. In 1856, the Army assigned him to survey the route of what is now U.S. 66 from Albuquerque to Los Angeles with the help of its newly imported camels.

Unlike the cowhands and muleskinners, Beale was not put off by the camels' strangeness and their insistence on being treated with care and respect. He learned all he could about them, observed them carefully and soon became enthusiastic.

"My admiration for camels increases daily with my experience of them," he said in his official report. "The harder the test they are put to, the more fully they justify all that can be said of them. . . . No one could do justice to their merits or value in expeditions of this kind, and I look forward to the day when every mail stage across the continent will be conducted and worked altogether with this economical and noble brute."

Beale tried to educate the men hired to work with the camels and made mistreatment of the animals a guardhouse offense. The chief result was that the guardhouse frequently was full of men who had disobeyed his order. Shortly before he was promoted and ordered to duty in Washington, he gave up and made a proposal that might have saved the experiment.

"Americans of the class seeking this employment," he wrote, "are totally unfit, harsh, cruel and impatient to the animals intrusted to their care. It would be advisable to hire Mexicans for the task, for they are more gentle and understanding in their treatment of animals."

This suggestion was ignored, but the Army did recommend bringing one thousand more camels into the Southwest. By then, however, the Civil War was beginning, so the project quickly faded. After Beale's departure the few score camels that had been brought in melted away into the desert, doubtless with help from camel haters.

All the Army's camels were of the Western Asian, one-humped, dromedary species. A group of San Franciscans who owned mines in Nevada thought that the two-humped Bactrians (*Camelus bactrianus*) of Eastern Asia might be preferable and imported twenty from China. A freighting company in British Columbia on the west coast of Canada also brought in a number of Bactrians. These did no better than the dromedaries, however. In fact, they frightened so many horses that both the Nevada and British Columbia governments eventually passed laws barring camels from public highways.

So the story of the camel's return to its original home is a sad one. It may have come very close to ending quite differently. Many of the Army's camels probably were shot by men with grudges against them, but some managed to survive in the deserts on their own and even to produce at least a few young. Occasionally, up until 1913 and later, reports were made of sighting wild camels in remote parts of Arizona and northern Mexico. Had a few dozen more been turned loose, wild camels might be on the way to rivaling wild horses in the remote reaches of the West.

CHAPTER SEVEN

The Loved and the Hated

NEARLY every recent year has seen publication in this country of a dozen or more books and several score magazine pieces about members of the species *Felis catus*, the domestic cat. Europe and much of the rest of the world are not a long way behind in literary output in this field. Fairly typical of the great mass of published material is one collection of reports by owners of cats about how their pets comfort them in times of sorrow.

"My cat ordinarily shows no interest when I take letters

from our mailbox at the front door," went one such report, "but one day he riveted his gaze on a letter and climbed up beside me when I sat down to open it. As I read, he licked my cheek and purred comfortingly in my ear. The letter contained news that a cousin of mine had suffered an arm fracture."

Another publication in this genre gives details of such cases as that of a cat which retrieves baby birds that fall from their nests and presents them, unhurt, to its mistress, a bird lover. Stories like these usually are published by, and certainly for, ailurophiles or cat lovers. Persons of the contrary inclination also exist and are known as ailurophobes. One of the most determined on record was a Chicago banker who paid ten cents for every dead cat delivered at his house and who advertised an offer of one hundred dollars to the man who should "kill the last nasty cat on earth."

The remarkable thing about the relations between humans and cats is that a high proportion of those who take any interest at all in the animals go to such extremes and that this has been true since early in the association of the two species. Even persons with scholarly intentions go a little haywire when they approach the subject of the cat. One pretentious tome on the animal, for instance, begins with the solemn misstatement that it is the world's oldest domesticated species. Actually, the cat was domesticated comparatively late, certainly long after the dog, goat, pig, sheep and cattle.

The place seems to have been Egypt and the time after 2000 B.C. Archeologists suspect that Egyptian storage granaries attracted rodents and that these in turn attracted the local wild cat, *Felis lybica,* a species still extant and clearly ancestral to modern domestic cats. For several centuries, the wild cats may have been allowed or encouraged to hang around the granaries to hunt rodents before anyone tried to make pets of them.

When the Egyptians finally got around to this, however, they went to extremes beyond those of the most wild-eyed modern ailurophiles. The latter attribute only human feelings and ideas to their cats. The Egyptians made gods of them. One Egyptian city, Bubastis, was sacred to the cat-headed goddess Bast and to cats in general and boasted several cat temples. At some periods in Egyptian history it was customary for the owners of cats that died to embalm the animal to prepare it for life in the next world. Then they went into mourning, shaving their eyebrows. An ancient Egyptian cemetery dug up in 1895 contained nearly 200,000 cat mummies. At another period anyone who killed a cat, accidentally or otherwise, forfeited his own life.

From Egypt the cat-keeping custom spread throughout most of Asia and Europe. In ancient Greece and Rome cats were popular, though less so than in Egypt, but during the Middle Ages they fell upon evil days. The idea somehow got about that they were in league with the devil. This was due in part to the cat's nocturnal habits, since in that superstitious period nighttime was considered evil in itself.

The cat's reputation led to horrible cruelty. In some areas it was a Lenten custom to roast cats alive. In other places they were dressed in monks' costumes, crucified and skinned alive. One locality celebrated Mardi Gras by tying a cat to a pole in a public square and having the whole populace join in whipping it to death.

The medieval Spanish penchant for superstition may have kept the early Spanish colonists of the New World from bringing along any cats. At least there seem to be no clear-cut records of domestic cats crossing the Atlantic until the founding of the English colonies in North America in the early seventeenth century. For nearly three centuries after that the role of the immigrant cat was decidedly minor and subdued. It had small chance of surviving in the wild without human protection, stuck close to home and received a minimum of attention, so little that there is no way of guessing at its numbers except that they must have been small.

Contrary to a good many homemade legends, domestic cats did not take up with native bobcats and produce hybrids. The two species belong to the same family but to different branches, the bobcats being of the *Lynx* genus rather than *Felis*. They are too far apart in genetic characteristics to interbreed successfully.

One legend says such interbreeding produced the so-called Maine coon cat, a rather big cat with coarse long hair. Actually, such characteristics almost certainly came from cats that were brought back from the Far East by New England sailors in the early nineteenth century. Except for a few oddities of that sort, until the end of the nineteenth century United States cats were what most people now call either alley cats or house cats.

Professional breeders of cats call them Domestic Shorthairs and list twenty different breeds based chiefly on color. But since the turn of the century, most of the interest of those who go in for breeds of cats rather than plain cats has centered on two types newly immigrant from Asia—the Persians and Siamese. Both have been reported by enthusiasts to be descended from species different from the ancestors of the alley cat, but zoologists find no evidence to support this. The Persians are simply the result of many generations of selective breeding for long hair, and the Siamese seem to have been produced by some fairly recent mutations.

In some circles cats of unusual breeds are status symbols, and this has encouraged breeding of dozens of different kinds of Persians and Siamese plus new ones such as the Burmese and Abyssinian. The names of both the latter are pure fancy. The Burmese developed almost entirely in this country, and the Abyssinian got its start in Europe.

But not one cat owner in a hundred goes in for pedigreed animals, which number only a hundred thousand or so in the United States today. For there has been a cat population explosion in this country in the last few decades along with the human one. According to estimates by pet food manufacturers, we now keep more than twenty million cats.

This suggests that we may not be quite so materialistic a people as we sometimes accuse ourselves of being. Cats simply are not utilitarian animals. Some of them will catch rodents occasionally, if and when they feel like it, but few are kept for that purpose. The encouraging fact seems to be that most cat-keepers keep cats not for what they can get out of them but just because they like them. This also, of course, is usually the reason for keeping dogs, but a good many more dogs than cats are kept for utilitarian reasons since some breeds of dogs will hunt, tend sheep or cattle and keep watch against intruders. A few people may feel compelled to assign human attitudes and interests to their cats, thereby making themselves seem a little silly to others, but it is a harmless foible.

CHAPTER EIGHT

The Gnaw-It-All's

ANIMALS that associate with humans are of two funda-
mentally different kinds. One, which includes all the
immigrant species covered thus far, is under human control
so long as it stays in that association. Some horses, longhorn
cattle and a few members of other species have escaped
control, but to do so they had to get away and stay away
from humans. Another, a quite different kind of immigrant,
stays very close to humans; in fact, it is largely dependent
on men for food, shelter and protection from natural enemies.
But it does not by any means submit to control.

By far the most successful of this kind are three species
formally known as *Mus musculus, Rattus rattus* and *Rattus*

norvegicus. They are better known as, respectively, the house mouse, the roof rat and the house rat, though the last also has a good many other names, some of the printable ones being Norway rat, gray rat, wander rat, wharf rat and sewer rat. These three species are among the chief beneficiaries of civilization.

Each apparently evolved deep in the wilds of central or northeastern Asia and spread thence with the help of men. First to be noticed were the mice. They moved in on the early farmers of Mesopotamia eight or nine thousand years ago when the development of agriculture made possible production of enough food to store some for future use instead of eating it immediately. The etymology of the word mouse is a good indication of the relation between that species and ours since we first got together. The word is easy to trace back through the Latin *mus* and ancient Persian *moosh* to even more ancient Sanskrit *musha,* which is derived from the Sanskrit verb meaning *to steal.* Although each weighs only an ounce or so, mice often grew so numerous that they stole enough to cause famine.

The roof rat (like the house or Norway rat, this one has several other common names such as black rat and Alexandrine rat) was next to learn of the easy pickings provided by men. No one is sure just when this species first began exploring beyond the region of eastern Siberia and Mongolia where it originated, though it may have reached Switzerland in prehistoric times. Anyway, it certainly turned up in Europe in the eleventh century, possibly having hitched rides thither in the ships of returning Crusaders. Being ten times the weight of mice, the rats quickly made names for themselves and more than earned the horror they inspired by helping to spread the plague during the epidemics that periodically decimated Europe.

Both house mice and roof rats may have been aboard the *Niña*, the *Pinta* and the *Santa Maria* and have strolled ashore in the New World even before any of the human passengers landed. Members of both species may have been aboard the *Mayflower*, too. Or if they missed these boats, they caught others that followed not far behind, for they were well known throughout all the early Spanish, English and French colonies.

The third member of the trio, the house rat, did not arrive in this country until 1775. In fact, it did not make itself known to any part of the civilized world until about fifty years before that. Since then, it has scored one of the most spectacular biological triumphs in the history of life on earth.

It all began in 1727 when a great horde of the creatures, suddenly and without warning, engulfed the city of Astrakhan on the northern shore of the Caspian Sea. They apparently had originated somewhere in eastern Siberia, and some unknown compulsion, perhaps of the sort that occasionally seizes lemmings, had driven them westward. They swept through Astrakhan, crossed the Volga River, reached Germany within a few months and England within a year. In 1775 their first known representatives landed in Boston, and the gang was all here.

The first order of business was a struggle for supremacy between the already well-established roof rats and the newcomers. It was not much of a struggle. Being a little bigger and heavier, the house rats almost invariably either killed the roof rats or drove them out of any coveted territory. Today, roof rats hang on only in a few areas, such as the Gulf Coast, which are too hot to suit most house rats. Both kinds come in many colors from black to light gray or tawny, so the only sure way of telling them apart is by their builds: roof rats have slender bodies, pointed muzzles and prominent ears; house rats, thick bodies, blunt muzzles and close-set ears.

Between house mice and house rats there has been little trouble, because the former stay out of the way of the latter. Just as rats evade humans by sticking to burrows too small for pursuit, so mice evade rats by sticking to still smaller holes. But both eat much the same sort of food—namely, whatever we humans make available to them.

But "eat" is not the only thing they do to what we make available. Their outstanding features are their four, chisel-like front teeth, two in the upper and two in the lower jaw. These grow at rates of up to four inches a year, and hungry or not, their owners have to keep gnawing to keep wearing the teeth down. They gnaw not only on food but also on fur-niture, electric cables, lead pipes, concrete walls, steel pylons, and anything else that gets in their way or arouses their curiosity. In fact, our very word "rodent" comes from the Latin verb *rodere* which means "to gnaw."

Not only did we provide the rats transportation to this hemisphere, plus food and shelter and plenty to gnaw on when they got here, we also cleared the way for them by making things difficult for some of their potential competi-tion. Among the most attractive of rodents are native American wood rats (*Neotoma cinerea* and others), some varieties having bushy tails and thick, soft fur that make them look like squirrels, which they also resemble in their habits. A little larger than house rats, they might have made things difficult for the newcomers, but wood rats find civilized man and his works distasteful and seldom will stay anywhere near settled areas.

The native white-footed mouse also is a little larger than the house mouse and could have put up some resistance to the invaders. And the white-footed mouse (*Peromyscus leucopus* and others) does not shun human dwellings all the time. During the winter it often will move into vacant summer cottages or little-used farm buildings. But when humans move back into the cottages, it soon departs and leaves the field to the house mouse. There is something about us the white-footed mouse simply does not care for if it has to take us in large doses. Perhaps we smell bad to it, or perhaps we make it nervous.

We certainly do not have any such effect on the house mouse, house rat or roof rat. For more than a century the first two have been well established from coast to coast, with the roof rat filling in wherever the house rat finds the climate not to its taste. Today, rodent experts of the U.S. Fish and Wildlife Service estimate that we feed and house some one hundred million house rats at a cost of a billion dollars a year. The experts also estimate that we board about three times as many house mice but, because they are so much smaller, are nicked by them for only about one third of a billion dollars a year.

No money ever was spent less willingly. Since the days of the legendary Pied Piper of Hamelin men have been battling rats with every conceivable weapon and beating paths to the doors of inventors of better mousetraps. Lately, much of the effort has gone into concoction of more and more subtle—also more and more lethal—poisons.

These have killed millions and millions of rats and mice,

but they have made little if any difference in the total population. Mice start breeding at the age of forty days, produce young nineteen days after mating, can mate again two days after that and have about six in a litter. One pair, if all its offspring survived, could have millions of descendants within a couple of years. Rats are almost that fecund, too. Consequently, if only a single pair survives an intensive poisoning campaign—or if a single pair wanders in from outside after the campaign ends—that pair quickly repopulates the area.

Lately, even professional killers of rats and mice have gotten around to admitting that they are up against difficult opposition. They used to call themselves exterminators. Now many prefer the term "rodent control specialist."

The overall effect of the centuries-old human war on rats may have been an improvement of the breed, or at least an improvement in its capacity to defy men. Many rats now are so suspicious that they seem able to detect and avoid the most cunningly poisoned baits. Others are incredibly brazen. A couple of years ago custodial officials in Washington, D.C., had to organize big campaigns to drive rats from the Washington Monument, the Jefferson Memorial and the office buildings of the House of Representatives. And every year most of the nation's larger cities have a few hundred cases of rats attacking and biting humans.

This sort of thing has brought about a sharp differentiation in human attitudes toward rats and mice. An incident reported by a Philadelphia rodent control man is a good example.

One morning he received a phone call from the lady of a house in a suburban development. She was nearly hysterical because she had found on her beautiful new kitchen counter several little black pellets. She had moved to the development from an older neighborhood where rats were plentiful, had been fervently thankful for being able to leave such neighbors and now felt sure that they had followed her.

When the expert she summoned examined the evidence, he was able to asure her that it consisted of the droppings not of rats but of mice. She almost wept with relief. Was he quite sure that it was not just small, young rats? He was quite sure. In that case she was terribly sorry to have bothered him.

"That's all right," he told her. "I do mouse work, too, and it's much the same sort of problem."

"Oh, no!" she replied in horror. "I couldn't let you do anything like that. Mice are cute."

This attitude is by no means yet universal, but it is shared by a large and apparently growing number of Americans. Mickey Mouse, Mighty Mouse and other such murine heroes of cartoons and comic books doubtless have a lot to do with it, but comic-book readers are not the only ones affected. Even so sophisticated a publication as *The New Yorker* goes along. One of its editorials has proclaimed:

"Rats are revolting, but we sort of like mice."

This does not make much sense. Mice almost never bite people, but the damage they do to human possessions is of the same kind as that done by rats. Although rats now outdo mice in terms of total damage, it is quite possible that wiping out rats would lead to such an increase in mouse numbers that mice would do even more damage than rats now do.

Not all mice and rats are destructive, however. A little more than a century ago medical researchers began noticing similarities between rats and mice on the one hand and humans on the other in terms of metabolism, nutrition requirements and other aspects. Today, there are millions of laboratory rats and mice, and several whole branches of medical research are heavily in debt to them.

Another quite different immigrant rodent also is of great importance in laboratory research. In fact, its use in that work is so well known that its name is a synonym for any creature or person used in an experiment. This is the guinea pig (*Cavia porcellus*), one of our few animal immigrants from South America, where it is native throughout most of the continent. Its name is a misnomer, the first part having been acquired because the first of the creatures seen in England were taken there by sailors who found them in Guinea and the second perhaps because, when hungry, it makes a sound something like a piggish "oink." The Incas of Peru domesticated guinea pigs as pets and for use as food. In North America they seldom are eaten by humans, but a good many are kept as pets.

Another immigrant rodent, the hamster from southeastern Europe and Asia Minor, also is popular here as a pet, though in its homeland it is considered a nuisance because of the damage it does to crops. Closely related to rodents, though of a different order, are the immigrant European rabbits. Domesticated by medieval monks, they usually are kept for food but also occasionally as pets. They have native American cousins, but these seldom live long in captivity.

More recently immigrant are two South American rodents brought here for their fur. One is the chinchilla (*Chinchilla laniger*) from the southern Andes. A creature about ten inches long, it has a squirrel-like tail, a rabbit-like head, big, round ears and a luxurious, silver-gray fur so fine that individual strands are invisible. Fur farmers have been raising it in this country with varying success since the 1920's.

The other is the coypu or nutria (*Myocastor coypus*), also

a south Andean native. Up to two feet in length and twenty or more pounds in weight, coypus are water dwellers and have fur something like the beaver's. Again and again in the last few decades, numbers of the animals have been released in various parts of the country in the kind of swampy areas they prefer. The idea has been to make those swamps produce valuable fur. They have produced some fur. But in parts of New Jersey, Oregon and several southeastern states the coypus have spread out into farming land and have wreaked havoc on crops. They seem to be solidly established, however, reportedly numbering millions, in the Gulf States.

Finally, there is a non-rodent immigrant in Hawaii which was encouraged to make itself at home there because of the immigrant rodents. This is the Indian mongoose (*Herpestes edwardsii*), a two-foot-long, weasel-like animal. Rudyard Kipling made it famous in *The Jungle Book* with his story of Rikki-tikki-tavi, the cobra killer, but it also is well known as a rat killer.

When descendants of house rats and roof rats that jumped ship in Hawaii began to make nuisances of themselves there, several pairs of mongooses were brought in and turned loose. The results were startling. The rats quickly learned to live in trees where they are comparatively safe from mongooses and where they can prey on tree-nesting birds, while the mongooses took up a diet of ground-nesting birds and poultry. Now the Hawaiians have two nuisances in place of one, both the rats and mongooses being firmly established there.

CHAPTER NINE

Birds of the Barnyard

IN CHARLIE CHAPLIN'S classic comedy, *The Gold Rush,* the little tramp and his partner are snowbound in a cabin deep in the wilds of Alaska. After several days without food the burly partner begins to have delusions. He keeps imagining that Charlie has changed into a plump, mouth-watering chicken.

The chicken as a symbol of a dream of edible glory has long been common in this country. In the 1920's those who felt sure that prosperity for all Americans was about to be achieved adopted the motto, "A chicken in every pot." Today, although places of deep and gloomy poverty still linger, this aim has progressed a long way toward realization. The average American eats about thirty pounds of chicken per year, which means that there is a chicken in nearly every family's pot once a week or oftener.

The bird (*Gallus gallus*) that made all this plentiful nutrition possible still exists in the wild state in its original home, the jungle that stretches from northern India across Burma and Thailand to Indo-China and Indonesia. Usually known as the red jungle fowl, it lives in flocks which spend much of their time on the ground scratching for food. Such flocks probably began fascinating and feeding primitive men far back in Stone Age times. By 2000 b.c. the men of the Indus Valley in northwest India had domesticated the jungle bird and also had learned to breed it for greater size.

In the following fifteen hundred years the practice of keeping chickens spread gradually westward throughout the Near East and the Mediterranean world. They were not always kept for eating purposes, however. Indeed, in many times and places it was taboo to eat the bird because of its use in religious rites of various kinds. At other times the chief use was for staging battles between cocks. And the early Romans thought they could get a line on the outcome of any planned venture by offering food to chickens. If the birds ate hungrily, the omen was good; if not, bad.

During the Middle Ages the importance of chickens as food increased steadily, and nearly all the early colonists of the New World brought along a few to start broods here. (Recent discoveries indicate that some Central American Indians kept domesticated chickens before Columbus, and it is possible that Polynesian seafarers may have brought them across the Pacific.) Those first American chickens probably did not differ much from the ones kept in the ancient world. Later, New England became a center of poultry breeding and developed such breeds as the Rhode Island Red, the Plymouth Rock and the New Hampshire, but it was a comparatively recent immigrant that founded the more important branch of the modern poultry industry.

By the 1830's a sizeable number of Americans were living in cities where they were unable to keep chickens to provide eggs, which long since had become a staple of the national diet. Farmers who supplied eggs to cities found the demand growing and sought a breed that would lay the maximum number. In 1835 the first Leghorn hens were brought from northern Italy for tryouts as layers. Descendants of these immigrants and others like them now are so lavish and the public so avid that the annual production of eggs is more valuable than chickens raised for the table (about $1,800 million compared with a little under $1,500 million). We eat almost an egg a day apiece for every man, woman and child in the country.

Nowadays, Leghorns kept for egg-laying are the most numerous of all pure-bred chickens raised here. Nearly all the birds raised by the highly efficient broiler industry are cross-mated. In addition, a few other breeds, such as the Brahma and Cochin from Asia and the Hamburg, Minorca and Houdan from Europe, have been brought here by fanciers, but none ranks very high in numbers or economic importance.

In those two respects, however, chickens in general far outrank all other birds. The runner-up is the turkey (*Meleagris gallopavo*). Everyone learns in grade school or earlier about how the Pilgrim fathers celebrated the first Thanksgiving with a turkey dinner, and that Benjamin Franklin thought it, rather than the bald eagle, should be our national bird. All this makes it startling to learn that the turkey we eat at Thanksgiving nowadays is descended mostly from immigrants.

The turkey the Pilgrims ate and Ben Franklin admired was a wild bird. Instead of doing much about domesticating it, our forefathers very nearly exterminated it (a few still can be found in some backwoods areas). The Aztecs, however, had domesticated a Mexican variety of turkey long before their conquest by the Spaniards, and the bird greatly impressed the Conquistadors. In 1502 they took the first pairs to Europe, where turkey raising quickly caught on and spread throughout much of the continent. By 1560 the growers were so successful that there is a record of a banquet in Germany in that year at which more than a hundred turkeys were served.

It was at this period that the bird acquired the misnomer by which we know it. The misnaming began when someone got the impression that it was the same bird as the guinea hen recently brought by the Portuguese to Europe from the west coast of Africa. That was then Moslem-dominated country, and to Europeans in those days, any Moslem country was Turkey. When domesticated turkeys were taken to the North American colonies in the following century, the name "turkie-fowle" went with them. Here the Mexican variety has occasionally been crossed with native birds, but most of our Thanksgiving bird's ancestors came from south of the border.

There are numerous other immigrant domesticated birds— guinea fowl from Africa, peacocks from India, canaries from (believe it or not) the Canary Islands, pigeons from Europe, budgerigars from Australia and parrots from the tropics around the world. But the only ones besides chickens and turkeys of much economic importance are ducks and geese.

In Europe and parts of Asia the latter generally outrank the former. Descended from the graylag goose (so called because of its habit of migrating later than other geese) of Europe and Asia and from the closely related Chinese goose, domestic geese (*Anser anser*) long have been favorites with some types of gourmets because they (the geese, that is) will keep overeating until their fat literally smothers them. *Pâté de foie gras,* made from the liver of a goose that has stuffed itself to death or has been forcibly so stuffed by its owners, is one of the results. Possibly because there always have been many other sources of fat in this country, geese never have been as popular here as in other parts of the world, though they have been raised here in small numbers since far back in colonial times.

All domestic ducks, except for a few kept in hot countries and miscalled Muscovy ducks (of the species *Cairina moschata,* native to South and Central America) are descended from the mallard (*Anas platyrhynchos*). This bird always has been plentiful in the wild state, but our domesticated variety of mallard, the white Pekin duck, comes from China. The first Pekins apparently did not arrive here until 1873. In that year a Connecticut man visiting in China bought a big flock of the ducks to take home. The voyage was a hard one. Only one male and two females survived, and they were in poor shape. They pulled themselves together, though, and within a few months presented their owner with some two hundred ducklings. Their descendants and those of later arrivals have been growing in popularity ever since.

CHAPTER TEN

Birds of the Gun Club

C HICKENS, turkeys and such may be good to eat, but raising them for the table is no fit work for a gentleman or, alternatively, a he-man. This, anyway, is the firmly held conviction of two otherwise quite different social groups which have had great influence on the attitudes of many Americans.

The first group consists of the English upper classes. For two or three centuries one of the articles of faith of this group has been that a gentleman shoots game birds. To be born a gentleman and yet disagree with this is to be branded an eccentric. The approved attitude is summed up in a famous line still to be heard all over England any fair morning in the hunting season:

"What a beautiful day! Let's go out and shoot something."

The second group consists of many tribes of American Indians among whom it used to be believed, and still is in some cases, that anything like farm work is for women and sissies and that a man's work is hunting.

The close coincidence of these two attitudes made it inevitable that many of the early settlers of this country would adopt similar outlooks. Indeed, so many adopted such views so enthusiastically that they long ago exterminated numerous kinds of native game birds. Wild turkeys, quail and several kinds of partridge and grouse persist only in small parts of the range they once occupied. Others, such as the passenger pigeon and the heath hen, have been completely wiped out.

Partly because of the depletion of native game birds and partly because they always were looking for new things to shoot, hunting enthusiasts began importing and releasing Old World game birds at least as early as 1790. In that year Richard Bache, son-in-law to Benjamin Franklin, released on his Delaware River estate several pheasants sent him from England. He hoped that they would nest and stock the countryside. As has happened countless thousands of times since then in similar efforts, the birds disappeared without a trace. Any wild animal turned loose to fend for itself in a new environment has small chance of surviving for very long the new predators, diseases and other adversities it must face.

Sportsmen intent on improving the shooting in their neighborhoods seldom bother their heads about such matters. When they get excited about game birds hunted in other parts of the world, they simply import a few pairs and hope for the best. Many state and local game commissions have gone in for the same practice.

A good example of how otherwise sane men can get carried away by this sort of thing is the widespread and long-lasting obsession with the European quail (*Coturnix coturnix*). A species quite different from the native American quail or bob-white (*Colinus virginianus*), this bird repeatedly has been turned loose in this country in large numbers. In the spring of 1877, for instance, the game commissions of six eastern states cooperated in importing and releasing several thousand pairs. Some pairs succeeded in nesting and raising broods, but in November all disappeared.

Their disappearance was quite predictable. They are migratory birds and habitually take a southeasterly course in their migration. With our eastern seaboard as their starting place, they inevitably perished in the open Atlantic. Sailors aboard a ship some three hundred miles southeast of Cape Hatteras were the last to see the birds. A few hundred nearly exhausted quail landed on the ship and rested briefly before continuing their hopeless flight.

The remarkable part of the migratory quail story is that that was only one of dozens of similar attempts to introduce the bird into this country. Such attempts still are made from time to time. The result always has been much the same as it was in 1877.

Altogether, more than eighty species of European, Asian, African and South American game birds have been turned loose in this country in numbers ranging from a few dozen pairs to several hundred thousands. Among them have been European corn crakes, Norwegian willow ptarmigan, Finnish capercaillie, bamboo partridges, Cyprian francolin, Scottish black grouse and Formosan teal—to name only a few of the most colorful. Millions of dollars of public and private funds have gone into such efforts. Few of the birds have had luck even as good as the European quail's.

In the case of three other game birds, however, persistence in introducing them here eventually led to success. The greatest has been that of the pheasant, a kind of bird which has no native American representatives but some thirty species and subspecies of which are scattered over Europe and Asia. It was the English variety (*Phasianus colchicus*) that Richard Bache tried to establish here in 1790, and for a century thereafter thousands upon thousands of the English birds were imported and turned loose, the results always being the same as Bache got.

In 1881 the American consul in Shanghai bought several pheasants of the Chinese variety and sent them to a friend in Portland, Oregon. Outwardly, the only noticeable difference between these birds and the English ones was that the Chinese cocks each had a ring of white feathers around its neck. Yet when the birds were turned loose in Oregon's Willamette Valley, they settled down to proliferating so rapidly that within a few decades ringnecked pheasants, or Chinese pheasants as they usually are called in the West, were the chief game birds in most parts of the northern half of this country and in much of Canada.

No one knows just why the immigrant Chinese pheasants should have had such success after the many failures of the English variety. Possibly some undetected quirk in metabolism or physiology made the difference. Perhaps it was only a matter of chance. The latter seems the more likely since English pheasants released about the turn of the century did fairly well in some parts of New England.

In the cases of the two other successful immigrant game birds the reasons for success are a little clearer. Hungarian partridges (*Perdix perdix*) were released in the Canadian province of Alberta in 1908. The soil, vegetation, climate and other factors were similar to those in which it had evolved. Also, the bird population cycle of the area was on an upswing. The partridges not only proliferated in Alberta but also gradually spread to nearby areas, and now are well established in several of the northern tier of states.

The story of the chukar partridge (*Alectoris graeca*) from Asia is quite different. By 1953 some 300,000 birds of this species had been turned loose in eastern and midwestern areas. None survived much more than a year or so. The bird's native habitat is arid, open country. But when chukars finally were released in the arid, open country of the Far West, they, too, caught on and proliferated.

In the last decade awareness has come to game-management men that there may be a connection between the kind of habitat in which a bird thrives in its native land and the kind of habitat in which it might survive here. Now studies are under way to find in other countries game birds that may do well in parts of this country where there are few native ones. The result may be some highly successful new immigrants in the next decade or so.

CHAPTER ELEVEN

Birds of the City Streets

BESIDES domesticated birds for plain eating and game birds for fancy hunting, men have been bringing to this continent for more than three centuries many different species of a third type of bird. Few of these feathered immigrants have found the New World to their liking. Three, however, have learned not only to like it but also to take full advantage of the great changes man has made in the continent and to spread all over it.

The first was brought here as a domesticated bird by

French settlers of Nova Scotia in 1606. For some unknown reason the only domestic animals these settlers brought along, besides a few chickens, were pigeons (*Columba livia*). The proprietors of the Virginia Company also thought highly of this bird and in 1621 sent to their colonists several pigeons "the preservation and encrease whereof we recommend unto you."

In both cases the species involved was the rock dove (the words pigeon and dove are synonymous), native to the coastal regions of much of Europe where it nests on cliff ledges. Domesticated at least as far back as the days of ancient Greece, it has been bred to produce several varieties such as homing pigeons, pouters and fantails. Although squab is a favorite dish in some parts of the world, it never has been very popular in this country, perhaps because of the abundance of native birds like the passenger pigeon in the old days and the mourning dove now. Besides, raising domesticated pigeons has never been more than a hobby here.

Since hobbyists tend to be fickle in their interests, immigrant pigeons have had many opportunities to escape captivity. Few have gone completely wild, though, because they have found the ledges of American city buildings quite as suitable for nesting as their native European cliffs. Indeed, the human enmity for hawks and other predators made such nesting sites safer than any the birds had known in the wild at home. This, together with our penchant for tossing animals scraps of food, explain the flocks of pigeons that frequent parks and other urban areas from coast to coast.

Just what explains the enthusiasm of those who feed and admire pigeons is a question public health officials are beginning to feel an urgent need to answer. That enthusiasm makes it extremely difficult to do anything about changing or repealing many state and local laws protecting pigeons. The reason public health men want the birds unprotected, indeed persecuted, is that they believe them implicated in the spread of such diseases as encephalitis and histoplasmosis. In some areas pigeon fans flatly refuse to believe this and make dire threats against health officers who utter anti-pigeon sentiments.

The second of the three immigrant street birds has no need either for feeding or protection. In the spring of 1847 Thomas Woodcock, president of the Natural History Society of Brooklyn, New York, received from England a crate containing several pairs of small, dingy birds. He released them in a city park. None survived the following winter. Woodcock repeated his experiment with a similar lack of success each of the following three or four springs. In either 1851 or 1852 his persistence was rewarded. The birds nested, raised several broods of young and wintered over in large numbers. The house sparrow (*Passer domesticus*) was here to stay.

Sometimes called the English sparrow, presumably because Woodcock got his specimens from Great Britain, it is neither English nor a true sparrow but a weaverbird that originated in Africa. On its own, it long ago spread over much of Europe and Asia. Once established with human help in Brooklyn, it immediately began a similar spreading over this continent. Within two years it was nesting from Philadelphia to Portland, Maine. Within twenty-five years it had reached the Pacific Coast and shortly thereafter was found in Hawaii and from Lake Athabaska in northern Canada to Cuba and the Bahamas.

One of the most pugnacious little birds in existence (it has been known to take angleworms away from robins five times its size), it also is highly adaptable. Colonies thrive in such varied locations as the southern coast of Greenland and California's Death Valley. During its first several decades in this country, one of its chief sources of food was the undigested grain in horse droppings. When that supply began to dwindle with the rise of the internal combustion engine, the birds switched to other sources. In summer, for instance, some of them often can be observed hanging around filling stations to pick up insects that fall off the radiators of cars stopping for gasoline.

In comparison with the starling (*Sturnus vulgaris*), however, the house sparrow has been only moderately successful in this country. The starling's adaptation to the continent as changed by man has been one long biological triumph. Some ornithologists think that it may now be the most abundant wild bird in the whole hemisphere. It has accomplished all this in only a little more than seventy years.

Shakespeare started the whole thing. In *Henry IV*, Part I, he has young Henry Percy, called Hotspur, say:

"I'll have a starling shall be taught to speak. . . ."

Three centuries after Shakespeare wrote this, a German-born American drug manufacturer named Eugene Schieffelin, who doted on Shakespeare, decided that he wanted to do something for both his adopted country and his favorite dramatist and that that something should consist of transplanting to the former birds of every species mentioned in the plays of the latter. Shakespeare had a word to say about a great variety of birds, and Schieffelin had plenty of funds to devote to his project. He devoted a lot of them to importing and releasing in and around New York City hundreds of pairs of skylarks, song thrushes, nightingales and others. None of these was able to survive here for very long.

Only the first showed any liking at all for the American way of life. In 1887 some of Schieffelin's skylarks settled down to building nests in the fields near what was then the Long Island village of Flatbush (now the heart of Brooklyn). For twenty years knowledgeable observers kept reporting that they had seen or heard skylarks in that neighborhood. The last report generally considered authentic, however, was recorded in 1907.

It was in the spring of 1890 that Schieffelin achieved his great success by turning forty pairs of imported starlings loose in Central Park. That success grows more noticeable every year. Many starlings spend their days foraging through the countryside, and at night return to cities and towns to roost where few predators dare follow. Such starling roosts —roofs, cornices and window ledges of public and private buildings—tend to be rather noisy and to accumulate the birds' droppings. Persuading them to go elsewhere is almost impossible. Neither shooting at them nor making loud noises repeatedly nor playing amplified tapes of starling distress cries nor administering electric shocks stays a really determined starling flock from swiftly returning to a preferred roost.

A discovery a few years ago by the custodian of the state capitol building in Springfield, Illinois, added something alarming to the starling menace. The custodian noticed that the capitol roof seemed to be sagging. He investigated. He found that the roof was holding up a collection of more than ten tons of starling droppings. Perhaps some way of keeping starlings away from buildings will yet be found. We have to hope so, because the starling population explosion seems almost to match the human one.

About the turn of the century the United States government began regulating the importation of foreign birds, but three new immigrant birds managed, presumably with human help, to establish small beachheads before the regulations went into effect. In and around St. Louis the European tree sparrow (*Passer montanus*), which looks much like the house sparrow, has made a place for itself. On New York's Long Island the colorful European goldfinch (*Carduelis carduelis*) can be seen in several communities. Also on Long Island and in the nearby lower Hudson Valley the mute swan (*Cygnus olor*) seems to be well entrenched. None of these, however, seems likely ever to imitate the pigeon, house sparrow or starling and spread across the land.

CHAPTER TWELVE

Water-Born and Borne
Across the Water

FRESH-WATER fish don't get around much, at least not between continents. Except for a few types like salmon, which actually spend nearly all their lives in the ocean, they are even more effectively barred from crossing salt water than are land animals. The fish need not only a boat but one that will hold a tankful of fresh water and keep it secure from contamination with salt water. And an intercontinental land bridge is of no use to them except in the highly unlikely event that there is a stream running across it.

With the help of humans, however, one species of fish confined to Europe and northern Asia until about one hundred years ago has immigrated with, from the biological point of view, sensational success. From the point of view of many humans who catch fish for pleasure, that biological success has been a sporting disaster. From the point of view of those who will have to feed our exploding human population a few decades from now, the sporting disaster may turn into a nutritional boon.

The fish is the carp (*Cyprinus carpio*). Plump and fast growing, carp were domesticated in China two thousand or more years ago, and they have been raised artificially in Europe since the early Middle Ages. One reason for this is that they do well in shallow ponds and thrive on slops from the kitchen. A properly tended pond will produce twelve hundred pounds of carp per year for each acre of surface area.

All this greatly impressed one of the leading men of nineteenth-century American science, Spencer F. Baird, secretary of the Smithsonian Institution. In the 1870's, on his recommendation, the U.S. Bureau of Fisheries imported several tankfuls of young carp from Germany and released them in streams in several parts of the country. Few secretaries of scientific organizations have earned more bitter denunciation for their efforts. In many streams and ponds throughout the country the fertile and adaptable but despised carp have blotted out native fish favored by sport fishermen.

One reason for the fisherman's dislike of carp is that when one of these fish is hooked it is unable to make much effort to escape and can fairly easily be hauled out of the water. This means the carp is not "game." Another count against it is that it has a muddy or otherwise unpleasant flavor and too many bones, though this is a matter of taste and of how the fish is raised and prepared.

More defensible are the objections to the effects of carp

population explosions on the waters where these occur. One of the most spectacular took place some years ago in Malheur Lake in southeastern Oregon. About 12,000 acres in area but not much more than a foot deep anywhere, this lake proved ideal for carp. By the fall of 1955 they had not only driven out or destroyed all other fish but also had eaten most of the vegetation so that they were near the starvation point. Since the lake is in a national wildlife refuge and since the plants growing there are important to migrating ducks and geese, the U.S. Fish and Wildlife Service undertook to eliminate the carp by poisoning the water. The poison killed an estimated 1,500,000 carp.

As suggested earlier, however, if our own population continues to grow at its current pace, Baird eventually may be vindicated. Even now, protein foods are in short supply throughout much of the rest of the world. As the Malheur Lake and other such experiences have demonstrated, carp are highly efficient organisms for turning vegetation into protein.

Although European roach and tench have been planted with some success recently in southern streams, the only immigrant food-fish of much importance, other than the carp, is the brown trout (*Salmo trutta*), a close relative of our rainbow and cutthroat trout. Native to the area stretching from Iceland to Algeria to the Himalayas, the brown trout can thrive in warmer, dirtier water than the rainbow will stand for and has been "planted" in streams in many parts of the country. Some blame it for having helped to exterminate the Michigan grayling and for making trouble for other American fish, but it seems to be here to stay.

Most of the other immigrant fresh-water fish can be eaten. In fact, a few years ago it was an inexplicable college-boy fad to swallow alive large numbers of one kind. Few other people get that hungry either for fish or for attention, though, and the general preference is to keep goldfish simply to look at.

This is not the case in their native land. The Chinese began domesticating goldfish (*Carassius auratus*) about a thousand years ago, apparently chiefly for food, and still raise them for that purpose just as they do carp, to which goldfish are fairly closely related. Those raised for food or left in the wild are a dark, dull silver, but early in their breeding experiments the Chinese began producing fish with pleasing golden hues and interesting shapes and keeping these in tanks for their esthetic appeal.

Because of the difficulty of keeping a goldfish bowl full and intact on the back of a pack animal or aboard a sailing ship, it took such fish several centuries to reach Europe. In 1728 someone sent the Lord Mayor of London a bowful, and these promptly began to spawn young fish. Soon, goldfish were the rage of the upper classes. By the time of the American Revolution goldfish bowls were standard equipment in well-to-do households all over Great Britain and much of Europe.

It apparently took another half century or more to get a bowlful across the Atlantic, but by about 1850 goldfish keeping was beginning to catch on in this country. The popularity of the practice has grown steadily ever since. In the last few decades it has expanded to include the keeping of many kinds of small tropical fish. Now, according to one estimate, some ten million families in the United States keep goldfish and tropical fish, often in huge, elaborate tanks that hold many different kinds.

Inch-long guppies (*Lebistes reticulatus*) from Trinidad and northern South America and in shades of red, orange, green and violet seem to be the most popular species. Silvery, black-banded, freshwater angel fish (*Pterophyllum eimekei*) from the Amazon Basin, and brightly colored paradise fish (*Macropodus opercularis*) from southern China also are numerous. The latter amuse their keepers by building nests of bubbles to hold their eggs. Altogether there now are more than one hundred and fifty immigrant species of freshwater tropical fish living in tanks in homes and schools.

Some enthusiasts seem unable to bear the sight of a fishless pool of water. Not long ago the Chase Manhattan Bank installed a Japanese fountain and pool in front of its new building in New York's Wall Street district. One night soon after the pool was filled with water an anonymous fish lover slipped in several goldfish. They proved a big attraction, but many of those attracted were the sort that cannot resist temptation to throw away their money. Most of what they threw in the pool were copper pennies, and it takes only a trace of copper to kill fish. At last report the bank's management had tired of fishing out dead fish, drained the pool and organized a publicity campaign to persuade its anonymous benefactor not to bring it any more fish when the pool should be refilled.

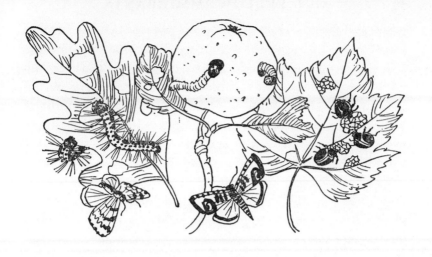

CHAPTER THIRTEEN

Mostly Unwanted

To most modern Americans, insects seem either fright-ening or disgusting or, at best, annoying. This attitude is by no means universal. In many parts of the world several kinds of insects are considered choice dishes, and there were times during the development of our species when insects made up most of the food of our ancestors.

But eating is by no means the only thing insects can be good for from the human point of view. Pollination of plants, aeration of the soil and reduction of dead tissue—these may not seem very important benefits, but if the insects that do these things were suddenly wiped out, the earth would not long remain habitable. Also, certain insects are unmistakably

75

harmful to humans and their enterprises. If other insects that attack these harmful ones were to cease their attacks, the harmful ones would swamp us no matter how deadly the insecticides with which we should fill the air. The species of helpful insects far outnumber the injurious.

Unfortunately, this does not hold true in regard to immigrant insects. Most of the well-known ones are decidedly harmful, some sensationally so. Only one is unmistakably helpful.

In these days of calorie counting and artificial sweeteners, it is hard to realize the importance of honey a couple of hundred years ago when it was our most common sweetener. Far back in prehistoric times men began risking being stung to death to get it. By the early days of ancient Egypt they had learned to provide artificial hives so that they could collect the honey less painfully. By the early days of the colonization of this country it was unthinkable for the colonists not to bring along their bees.

The chief species of honey bee, *Apis mellifera,* is native to Europe and has several varieties of which the comparatively gentle Italian one is the most important immigrant. By 1623 the newcomer bees were so plentiful in Massachusetts that swarms were able to escape and make hives for themselves in hollow trees. From then on westering settlers were able to look forward to wild bee trees throughout much of the country. More than one pioneer was at least as hopeful of finding a better bee tree over the next hill as of finding greener grass.

Our bee population has grown fairly steadily since those days, and the U.S. Department of Agriculture recently estimated that there were nearly six million colonies of honey bees in the country. Although honey no longer is as important as it once was, the bee's pollinating activity is even more so. Some fifty crops, such as clover, onions, apples, cherries and oranges, depend in whole or in part on honey bees for pollination, and the effect of insecticides on bees makes it necessary for many farmers to think twice about overdoing their spraying of poison.

Another immigrant insect with a great reputation for helpfulness actually doesn't deserve much of it. This is the Oriental praying mantis (*Paratenodera sinensis*), which arrived here from China in the 1890's. About four inches long, it usually stands rigidly still and holds its front legs in what seems like a praying position but would better be called preying, because the reason for the position is that the legs are ready to strike out and grab the first prey that passes. That prey is other insects.

First noticed near Philadelphia in 1896, the Oriental mantis has spread over much of the eastern part of the country and in some unknown way has acquired a quite remarkable reputation. There are many people who will solemnly assure you that the mantis does such great work in destroying other insects that anyone caught harming one will be fined $50. No such law ever has been passed or ever is likely to be. Mantises destroy at least as many helpful insects as harmful ones.

Many immigrant insects with reputations for hurtfulness do most definitely deserve those reputations. In fact, about half our most destructive insect pests are from abroad. One of the first to arrive was the codling moth (*Carpocapsa pomonella*), a native of Europe. Eggs of this moth may have come here in the first barrel of apples or the first bundle of apple or pear tree shoots brought over by Virginia or Massachusetts colonists. So long as apple and pear trees remained comparatively sparse and scattered, codling moths were the same, and their larvae (often called appleworms) riddled only a few apples and pears. But by the end of the nineteenth century huge orchards were the farming fashion in many parts of the country. So, inevitably, were huge infestations of codling moths. Planting vast, solid stands of apple and pear trees had on the codling moth population the same effect that gasoline has on a fire.

In the 1920's and '30's the orchard owners' response led to the nation's first great insecticide controversy, one that closely paralleled the current debate. It began when agricultural experimenters found that lead arsenate killed codling moths, and the orchard owners took up spraying their properties three or four times every summer. During one period the Wenatchee, Washington, area, a leading apple-growing section, used an average of seven million pounds of lead arsenate per year. Eventually, sizeable amounts of lead arsenate residues began to be found on fruit in the markets.

Alarmed public health authorities set limits to the permissible amount of such residue. Hard-pressed orchard owners retorted with evidence that humans can tolerate considerable amounts of lead arsenate. Others argued that the long range, cumulative effect of the poison was unpredictable but almost certainly dangerous. Then the codling moth developed tolerance for lead arsenate, and the amount of spraying necessary to kill the insect became prohibitively expensive for many orchard owners. At that point the insecticides currently in use became available, and the lead arsenate question was replaced by similar questions raised by the late Rachel Carson in her famous book, *Silent Spring*.

Another early immigrant insect is one of the most widely feared and detested of all our fellow newcomers on this continent. This is *Blatella germanica,* the German cockroach.

It is the one native of that land to achieve the goal to which so many other of its natives have aspired—the goal of world conquest. Today, a little carelessness in almost any part of the globe is likely to result, when someone suddenly turns on a light in a dark kitchen, in the sight of a number of half-inch-long, straw-colored creatures darting for the nearest crevices.

One of the few places where these creatures are not known as German cockroaches is Germany. In the northern part of their homeland they are called Swabian roaches. In the southern part they are called Prussian; in the eastern part, Russian; and in the western part, French.

Cockroaches can do their worst, spreading disease organisms, only if they are given plenty of opportunity in the form of negligent sanitation practices. Many other immigrant insects do their dirty work without help from the slovenly. The descendants of the playthings of a certain French astronomer, for instance.

In 1868 Leopold Trouvelot accepted a teaching post at the Harvard Observatory in Cambridge, Massachusetts. As many Frenchmen in those days, he made a hobby of raising silkworms, and he brought along for experimental purposes some eggs of a moth related to the silkworm. When these eggs hatched, a few caterpillars crawled out a window and proceeded to colonize New England. Known in their adult stage as the gypsy moth (*Porthetria dispar*), these caterpillars eat the leaves, sometimes nearly all the leaves, of many kinds of trees. Millions of dollars have been spent combatting them, but they have spread little by little as far south as New Jersey and as far west as Ohio.

New Jersey was the apparent starting point for colonization by another insect immigrant. In 1916 an entomologist noticed a few plump, shiny beetles of a metallic greenish brown color in a nursery near Riverton, New Jersey. It took him some time to find out what they were. When he finally made sure that they were from Japan, accidentally brought here on some nursery plants, he was not alarmed, because he also learned that in Japan the beetles were not at all pestiferous.

Within a couple of years, however, it developed that in this country the Japanese beetle (*Popillia japonica*) was going to be a nasty pest, indeed. Facing few of the natural enemies that controlled it at home, it multiplied rapidly and attacked a wide variety of crops with voracious appetite. It also began to spread. Now, although insecticides and other measures to keep down its numbers have been developed, it seems to be solidly established from Maine to Florida and as far west as the Mississippi River.

Altogether, more than a hundred species of insects have immigrated in the last three or four centuries and become pests here. The Hessian fly in the winter wheat fields of the Great Plains, the fire ant in the Southeast, and the European corn borer moth nearly everywhere east of the Rockies are among the more destructive. Stringent quarantine measures have been adopted to prevent others from joining them, but with intercontinental travel on the current scale, it is unlikely such measures will be completely effective. Insect larvae can turn up in the least likely places.

The ecologist Charles Elton tells a story about an acquaintance who bought a shirt in Egypt. When the shirt owner returned to his home in England, he discovered that tiny beetles were hatching out of the shirt buttons. Investigation revealed that these had been made from nut shells in which the eggs had been embedded before the nuts left their trees. Against hitchhikers of such persistence as that, no quarantine can permanently prevail.

CHAPTER FOURTEEN

Most Unwanted

ONE of man's oldest and most cherished daydreams is the fantasy of being invisible and able to pry into all sorts of matters and to influence the outcome of many conflicts. For a large number of creatures that dream has long been reality. Until three hundred years ago no one even suspected their existence. Even after they began to be noticed, it was two centuries before anyone grasped either their pervasiveness or their power in human affairs. Today, many have been made visible and shorn of their power, but others continue to dodge notice and wreak unpredictable havoc.

They are the microbes, the smallest living things. As in the case of insects, many are helpful to humans and some indispensable; great numbers of harmless bacteria live in our intestines and, among other things, help protect us against invasion by harmful ones. By far the greatest number of microbes have little or nothing to do with us or our affairs. Since the days of Louis Pasteur and Robert Koch, however, we gradually have come to understand that some of them are our deadliest enemies.

Among these are great travelers even more difficult to persuade to stay put than insects. Wherever man goes, they seem to yearn to follow. Although it now is impossible to determine which ones, some of them must have accompanied the earliest human immigrants from Siberia. But many famous ones did not reach the New World until after Columbus's voyages of discovery.

It is possible that many of the latter had not yet evolved into existence by the end of the last Ice Age when the Siberia-to-Alaska land bridge was inundated. Up to that point the human population of the Old World was sparse, and microbes preying on humans had little to work with. With the subsequent invention of agriculture and civilization, the human population boomed. The man-eating microbe population boomed, too, and developed many new forms.

In the New World the human population remained comparatively sparse, and few American Indians had had any chance to develop defenses against the immigrant microbes that accompanied Columbus and the Conquistadors. One of the first to make itself noticed was the virus of smallpox. It had been circulating through the Old World for centuries, killing many people and disfiguring more. About 1510 A.D. it started killing American Indians. Few mass killers have been more effective. According to one survey of available

evidence, smallpox wiped out more than half the total estimated American Indian population of six million.

Some tribes never did succeed in acquiring resistance to
the virus. When the huge wave of European immigrants
pushed westward across the country in the eighteenth and
nineteenth centuries, the migrants learned of the Indian's
great susceptibility. To those who believed that the only good
Indian was a dead one, this knowledge suggested a form of
germ warfare. It became common practice to make presents
to Indians of the clothing and blankets of settlers who died
of smallpox, a practice partly responsible for the almost
complete obliteration of some tribes of Plains Indians, such
as the Mandans and Assiniboins.

Another of the Old World's great killers did not find its
way across the Atlantic until 1832. It is a vibrant little bac-
terium which looks something like a wriggling comma and
because of its appearance is called *Vibrio comma*. Somewhat better known is the name of the disease it inflicts on
humans—cholera. Nowadays, that name does not mean much
in this country. It has been several decades since the last
known case of the disease here. But between 1832 and 1873
it repeatedly terrorized the nation and emptied cities of
citizens fleeing its embrace.

Four great cholera epidemics swept through this country,
in 1832, 1849, 1866 and 1875. Each time everyone could see
it coming a long way off, because each time the disease
started out from its home on India's Ganges River, spread
slowly westward across Europe and crossed the Atlantic
in steerage along with some of the poorer human immigrants.
In the first two American epidemics a great many people, including most of the medical profession, considered the disease a divine retribution for the moral failings of the victims.

The fact that the disease took its greatest toll in the filthiest, most lurid slum districts made this easy to believe.

The most remarkable thing about the story of cholera in this country is that by 1866, seventeen years before the famous bacteriologist, Robert Koch, indentified *Vibrio comma* as the cause of the disease, a working majority of the medical profession and reform-minded ministers had outgrown the superstitious explanation. That majority blamed the incredible filth of the cities, which had no sewage systems, got water from open wells and left garbage disposal to free-wandering pigs. When reformers forced a cleanup in New York City at the start of the 1866 epidemic (one item was the removal of some 160,000 tons of manure from vacant lots), the epidemic petered out there. It was one of the first great triumphs for advocates of public health laws. Koch's subsequent discovery showed how right the reformers had been: *Vibrio comma* is a denizen of the human intestine and can spread from one person to another only via contaminated food or water.

Other types of disease organisms still make their ways here from time to time, and it seems that little or nothing can be done to discourage their immigration. These are the influenza viruses. Although mild flu or something very like it has been known in Europe since the Middle Ages, it is in our century that it has made itself most felt and most feared. At the end of World War I a pandemic of virulent flu broke out on the Western Front and spread throughout the world. An estimated 500,000,000 people caught the disease, nearly half the earth's population, and it is possible that more than 30,000,000 died, mostly of pneumonia caught because of the weakening effect of the flu. In this country there were some 20,000,000 cases and 850,000 deaths.

That pandemic subsided almost as swiftly as it rose, but new kinds of flu viruses have been turning up occasionally ever since. The latest is the Asian variety which got its start in China in 1957. It first turned up in southwestern China in February of that year and reached here by fall. Despite a nationwide campaign of immunization, there again were some 20,000,000 cases, though far fewer deaths than in 1918 because of improved means of combatting pneumonia and other side effects.

Where our next immigrant microbe will come from and what kind of disease it will inflict, no one can guess. For man-eating germs, the human population explosion is providing an endless, world-wide feast. Mutations constantly occur among the microbes, and when a successful one turns up, jet planes may distribute it around the world before anyone realizes it is something new. It is quite possible, though, that it will be no worse than Asian flu.

But man-eaters are by no means the only immigrant microbes. The virus that causes hoof-and-mouth disease in cattle, for instance, has made its way here several times and from widely different directions—from Asia, from Europe and from South America. So far it has been repulsed and driven back out every time it got in, though often at very great cost in the destruction of herds of infected cattle.

The immigrant fungi that cause the chestnut blight (*Endothia parasitica*) and Dutch-elm disease (*Ceratostomella ulmi*), however, have not proved repulsable despite the millions of dollars spent fighting them. The chestnut-blight fungus arrived on nursery plants from Asia at the turn of the century and has long since wiped out our native chestnut trees, once the pride of the forests of many eastern states. Though not quite so rapid in its destruction, the elm bark fungus which arrived from Europe about 1910 now also seems unstoppable.

Eventually, though, some types of disease-carrying microbes may receive encouragement to immigrate. One of the chief alternatives to using ever larger amounts of ever more poisonous insecticides is the encouragement of diseases of insects. In the case of the Japanese beetle, some bacteria that turned up accidentally in New Jersey have proved far more effective than any of the poisons. The bacteria (*Bacillus popilliae*) cause what is called the milky disease in the beetle's grubs and have drastically reduced their numbers in many areas. Some entomologists think that a world-wide search for microbes that will attack others of our too-successful immigrant insects is the best hope of controlling them permanently.

CHAPTER FIFTEEN

From the Other Kingdom

THE LAST chapter crossed without warning from one to the
other of the two main divisions of living things via a
couple of minor divisions of the living and near-living. Up to
the microbes all immigrant species considered have been
members of the animal kingdom. Most biologists classify such
microbes as the protozoans that cause malaria and the
bacteria that cause cholera in a sub-kingdom called Protista
(Greek for "the first ones"), and they class viruses like those
that cause smallpox and influenza in another subordinate
group, the Microtatobiotes ("smallest living things"). But
microbes like the fungi involved in the chestnut blight and
Dutch elm disease belong, together with their victims, to the

other great kingdom, the plants. (It should be added that a few biologists think bacteria belong in the plant kingdom and protozoans in the animal kingdom, biologists being as prone to disagree among themselves as any other group of experts.)

Plants often have succeeded after immigrating here even more spectacularly than animals. In fact, throughout the world it is the newcomers among plants that have had by far the greater success. The case of the cultivated sunflower (*Helianthus anuus*) is typical.

Its ancestors are native to this country and grow wild in the Great Plains. In Central Europe, southern Russia, Peru and some other parts of the world, vast fields of the cultivated variety are grown for the valuable oil in their seeds. Every once in a while someone tries to grow it commercially in its native Kansas or Iowa. Often it does well the first year and fair the second, but by the third or fourth year the crop is a total failure.

As the botanist Edgar Anderson explains in his remarkable book, *Plants, Man and Life*, the sunflower fails as a commercial crop here *because* its ancestors are natives. During the time it evolved here, there also evolved along with it various insects, fungi, bacteria and other life forms that could live on it. Growing wild, sunflowers are scattered so that only a few of these parasites find each plant; but grown as a crop solidly filling several acres, the plants produce such a population explosion among their parasites that these become overwhelming within a year or two. Throughout the area where the sunflower originated, a reservoir of sunflower pests and diseases is always ready to produce such an explosion whenever the plants become plentiful.

The further sunflowers get from their native land, the

fewer such pests they encounter. A few insect eggs or fungus spores may travel with them unsuspected among the seeds, and a few pests native to their new homes will adapt to them; but the total of these is far fewer than those that grew up with them. And the same is true of other plants. As Dr. Anderson points out, all the world's great crop plants originated in places other than those where they have attained their great importance.

This "importance," of course, is as seen from the human point of view, and from that viewpoint the great crops are indeed indispensable. You might think that their value would long since have led to thorough study of the origins of those crops. It has not done so. Their origins are so fantastically tangled and have been so little investigated that much more is known about the origins of many domesticated animals than of most domesticated plants.

As we have said, it is well established, for instance, that the dog was the first animal domesticated, but no one is sure even which type of plant was first. Once it was taken for granted that one or another of the most valued food plants—perhaps a cereal grain like barley—had to be first. Study of modern primitive tribes who live and presumably think much the way Stone Age men did has led to doubt of this. Now many authorities suspect that the first domesticated plant may have been a flower raised to scare away devils, a spice like turmeric for use as a body paint or a kind of yeast for use in making beer and wine (yeasts are members of the fungus branch of the plant kingdom).

Even the history of maize (*Zea mays*), or as we usually call it in this country, corn, remains obscure. It has been grown by men throughout much of this hemisphere for at least several thousand years. Until a few years ago it had long been taken for granted that it had descended from a wild Central American grass called teosinte. Now it has been established that in all probability teosinte actually is descended from corn, a result of a chance crossing of corn with another wild grass, and it begins to seem possible that the true ancestor of corn has completely disappeared.

Corn was the leading crop of most North American Indian tribes and reached them from the south long before Columbus's voyages across the Atlantic. Other pre-Columbian immigrants from the south include squash, pumpkins, peanuts, tobacco and sweet potatoes, but two of the most important after corn only reached this country long after 1492 and via wide detours. These are the white potato (*Solanum tuberosum*) and the tomato (*Lycopersicon esculentum*). Their routes were quite different.

So many kinds of wild white potato now can be found scattered all the way from Mexico to Chile that it has not yet been determined which, if any now extant, is ancestor to the domesticated one. The latter certainly became highly important to the Indians of the Andes far back in prehistoric times. It meant so much to those of southern Peru that their language, Aymara, has 209 terms for the different kinds of potato. *Hantha,* for instance, means "an old potato with black skin and white flesh." Other terms indicate where the particular potato referred to grows best or how well it resists frost, and so on.

Not until toward the end of the sixteenth century, however, did any of the Conquistadors or their successors take enough interest to carry a few potatoes back to Spain. To men as hungry as many Europeans were much of the time in those days the new food was a great boon, and its popularity gradually spread through all the northern countries. By the early eighteenth century it was becoming Ireland's all-important crop. The first crop grown in this country seems to have been planted by Irish immigrants to New Hampshire in 1719. It soon caught on and became one of our important foods, though never quite as important as in Europe, which still grows about nine-tenths of the world's total.

The tomato's way here was even slower and more round-about. Low-growing Peruvian vines which produce fruit about the size of currants seem to be its ancestor, but it was Mexican Indians rather than Peruvians who increased the size and grew it widely, before Columbus. Taken to Spain at about the same time as the potato, it stirred little interest until it reached Italy. There it gradually became an important part of the national diet, perhaps in part because someone had the inspiration of calling it the love apple.

In the 1780's Thomas Jefferson, always ready to try something new, brought a few plants back from Europe. To a nation still in the grip of Puritanism, however, the term love apple meant that the fruit was certainly sinful and possibly poisonous. That reputation clung to the tomato in this country until about the World War I period. Probably the great wave of human immigrants from Italy in the early decades of this century had much to do with changing it, since they brought along both their passion for tomatoes and a number of improved varieties. Now tomatoes are so nearly ubiquitous here that it is hard to realize they were little more than slightly dangerous curiosities a few generations ago.

Great though the contribution of plant immigrants that originated to our south undoubtedly is, those that got their start across the Atlantic are still more important to us. The parade here of the latter started with Columbus's second voyage and was assisted by subsequent explorers. Nearly all those early transatlantic voyagers brought along and planted seeds from home.

In the words of the sixteenth-century English explorer and historian, Richard Hakluyt, Columbus brought on his 1493 voyage not only domesticated animals but also "wheate, barley, rye and pease to sowe, besides vines, plants and seedes of such trees, fruits and herbes as those countreys lacke."

Fifty years after Columbus, the French explorer, Jacques Cartier, sailed up the St. Lawrence River and reported: "We sowed seeds of our country as cabbages, turnips, lettuces and others, which grew and sprung up out of the ground in eight days."

Forty years after Cartier, Hakluyt reported receiving from a British fisherman who had landed on Newfoundland a letter saying: "I haven in sundry places sowen Wheate, Barlie, Rie, Oates, Pease and seeds of herbs, kernels, Plumstones, nuts, all of which prospered as in England."

Of the cereal grains among these, barley (*Hordeum vulgare*) and wheat (*Triticum vulgare*) probably were the first to be domesticated, well back in Neolithic times, and oats (*Avena sativa*) and rye (*Secale cereale*) the latest. The two latter probably first came to human attention as troublesome weeds cluttering fields of barley and wheat. Bit by bit, early farmers learned to use these weeds and, eventually, to plant them in pure stands.

All four are descended from species native to various parts of central and western Asia and eastern Africa. Rice (*Oryza sativa*) comes from southeastern Asia, and sorghum (*Sorghum vulgare*), which recently has increased greatly in importance, from Africa and India. Though all immigrated in several different forms, wheat has come here in especially great variety, because it is descended from at least three different species of two separate genera. This has made possible many different kinds of offspring.

Wheat growers in various parts of the Old World long ago began developing those differing offspring by raising the grain in widely differing soils and climates. Later, they found that some kinds of wheat made better bread, some better macaroni, some better pastry, and so on. Still later, some kinds proved more resistant to one or another of the various diseases that attack wheat. As a result, nearly every one of the early groups of human immigrants who planned to raise wheat here brought a different variety. In this century, the U.S. Department of Agriculture has sent plant explorers throughout the world seeking still more kinds. The upshot is that hundreds of different wheats now grow here, and the enormous annual yield resulting from their variety is one of the chief reasons why, unlike many of the world's other peoples, we have to worry not about too little food but about too much.

The steps by which our ancestors learned to make use of the cereal grains must have been fairly numerous. Presumably, they began by eating the seeds raw or parched, an undertaking which requires a cast-iron stomach, and only later learned to grind them and cook them into porridge, bread and other dishes. Learning to use most of our other vegetable foods was far simpler. There are hundreds of plants with nourishing and easily digestible roots, stems, leaves, flowers or fruits, and some began feeding our ancestors millions of years ago. A good many native North American plants can and occasionally do feed us now, but for the same reason that large solid plantings of native sunflowers fail, none is of much importance to us. All our great vegetable and fruit crops are immigrant.

Oddly, the more an immigrant vegetable or fruit has thrived here, the lower the United States human immigration quota is likely to be for the region from which the plant came. Peas and carrots, for instance, have been traced back to Afghanistan. Celery and beets have ancestors scattered around the Mediterranean. Cucumbers come from India, spinach from Persia, lettuce and asparagus from Asia Minor. Only the likes of Brussels sprouts and rutabagas come from the high-quota lands of northern Europe.

Even the last two are of northern Europe only in the sense that they attained their modern forms in that region. They belong to a genus, *Brassica,* which has provided us many other vegetables—cabbage, turnips, broccoli, cauliflower, kale and kohlrabi, to name only the best known. Some wild species of this genus are Asiatic, some from the Mediterranean area. Nearly all the table vegetables they have yielded developed from them within historic times, so that their origins are far better known than those of many other crops. Most of them reached this country by the seventeenth century, though broccoli did not catch on here until a few decades ago. Rutabagas, which also are called swedes or Swedish turnips, had the help of the always experiment-minded Thomas Jefferson in their immigration.

One of the earliest fruit immigrants was the watermelon (*Citrullus vulgaris*). Wild relatives still grow in the Kalahari Desert in Southwest Africa, and the modern types clearly are descended from them. The Indians of our Southwest were the first to grow them here, the seeds presumably having reached the area via Spain and Mexico.

But nearly all our more important fruits are of the class

known as temperate zone perennials. Among them are pears and plums from Central Asia, peaches and apricots from China and cherries from Asia Minor. The only notable exceptions are subtropical oranges and lemons from Southeast Asia and the grapefruit, which seems to have developed in the West Indies out of stock taken there from Malaya.

Until the rapid rise of the citrus fruits in the last couple of decades, however, the apple (*Malus sylvestris* and others) far outranked them all, and if all the backyard trees are taken into account, we probably still eat more apples than any other single fruit. Apples are similarly popular throughout most of Europe and in many parts of Asia. In this respect all of us are faithful to traditions begun by our remote ancestors. It is quite possible that men have been eating apples for a hundred thousand years or more.

We also have been helping the trees to spread all that time, at first by unthinkingly scattering the cores and for the last ten thousand years or so by deliberately planting the seeds. Such spreading has resulted in so much crossing and recrossing of different species and varieties that it is now impossible to trace the ancestry of modern apples. It seems likely, though, that many of the ancestors grew in the vast region stretching from eastern Turkey over the Caucasus Mountains to Turkestan. Their European descendants reached this country early in the seventeenth century and found nearly all of it much to their liking. They now number hundreds of varieties here, grow in a wide range of soils and climates and bear fruit at any time of year from early summer to to late fall.

Grapes, too, have been a favorite food for humans since far back in prehistoric times. All Old World grapes belong to a single species (*Vitis vinifera*) probably native to the

Caucasus region, though the number of varieties is large, but their story in immigration is quite different from that of most other immigrant fruits because several other species of grapes (*Vitis labrusca, Muscadinia rotundifolia,* etc.) are native to this country. The Puritanism of many of the early human immigrants included teetotalism, which meant that to them grapes were for eating only. They soon learned to like some of the native grapes for that purpose. But since time immemorial, many men have believed that the only sensible purpose for grapes is winemaking. Immigrants of this persuasion tended also to be strong in their taste prejudices; they turned up their noses at native grapes for winemaking.

Since diseases endemic among American grapevines in the eastern part of the country made it impossible to grow Old World grapes there, little winemaking was done here until the middle of the nineteenth century. This gave beer and whiskey their great head start in popularity among the nation's drinkers. But not long after the discovery of gold in California came another discovery many consider far more important; namely, that Old World grapes could be grown there with great success. Since then, California has become one of the world's great winemaking centers. A few much smaller centers recently have developed in New York and other eastern states as a result of crosses of immigrant vines with native species.

There are a number of less common immigrant fruits such as dates from the Persian Gulf, figs from Asia Minor, avocados from Central America, persimmons from China and pomegranates from Persia. And a few fruit trees, such as the famous Japanese cherries and different types of flowering crabapples, have been brought here not for their fruit but for their blossoms. Other immigrant trees include the Norway maple, the Lombardy poplar and the Chinese gingko.

Many of our flowers, shrubs and lawn grasses are immigrant, too. In *Plants, Man and Life,* Dr. Anderson suggests a way of getting an idea of how many of the plants in any neighborhood are of Old World origin. Because of the often violent and sudden change to winter weather during the North American autumn, native plants have so evolved that they color brightly just before their quick lapse into winter dormancy. European plants do not go through such a sudden or brilliant color change. Looking around in mid-autumn, you easily can tell the natives from the newcomers.

In one type of plant, however, the relation between native and immigrant ancestry is far from clear. Cotton has been grown for human purposes in the Old World for at least five thousand years. It has been grown for the same purposes in South and Central America for a not much shorter period of time. Both kinds of cotton belong to the genus *Gossypium* but otherwise are quite different, and for a long time it was taken for granted that they had evolved separately. Now, however, genetic studies indicate a possibility that the two kinds of cotton are fairly closely related. Much work remains to be done on the study of this relationship, but it may be that some seeds somehow crossed the Atlantic long before Columbus.

Useful plants like cotton and our fruits and vegetables are by no means the only immigrants. Numerous other species have come here as uninvited hitchhikers and have settled down with great success. We usually call them weeds, but that word is slippery.

About the only way to define a weed is as a plant growing where it is not wanted. The trouble with this is that different people want different things. The dandelion (*Taraxacum officinale*) is typical. Some homeowners on finding these in their lawns call it by worse names than weed, but others use the young leaves as salad greens, cook the older ones as they would spinach, make wine from the flower heads and are quite pleased to have the plants around.

No matter what our attitude toward them, though, most successful immigrant weeds owe us a great deal. The seeds of any plants new to an area rich in plant life are at a great disadvantage in competing with plants native to that area for space in which to put down roots and send up stalks and leaves, because the native plants have evolved in relation to each other in such a way as to occupy every inch of usable space. We humans break up such tightly interlocking relationships by digging foundations, building roads, cutting forests and ploughing fields for crops. The most successful weeds are those that produce tiny seeds which travel around with men unsuspected, in the cracks of packing cases, on muddy boots and in other such hiding places. They thus are right on hand when we break new soil.

One area where such successes have been spectacular is the coast of southern California. According to Dr. Anderson, the bulk of plants in the grasslands there are immigrants that began arriving with the earliest Spanish explorers and settlers. They are weeds, such as wild oats of several kinds, wild radishes and fennel, descended from plants which began evolving to take advantage of man's effect on the soil far back in early Mesopotamian times when that effect was just beginning to be important. In this respect they are something like the rats, mice, house sparrows, starlings and other animals for which we also have carved living space.

Even more like the cases of the house sparrow and the

starling is that of Florida's water hyacinth (*Eichhornia crassipes*). In 1884 a New York dowager visiting in New Orleans happened to see some of these attractive plants at a Venezuelan exhibit in a fair there. She bought three and planted them in a pond on her estate in St. Augustine. They prospered there and eventually spread to the nearby St. John's River. Now they so clog the river and other waterways that hundreds of thousands of dollars have been spent in fighting a losing battle against them.

Some botanists think it miraculous that much more of the country has not been overgrown long since with weeds like Florida's water hyacinths and California's wild oats. Not only private individuals but even government agencies have brought seeds and cuttings by the thousands to this country. Twenty years ago the U.S. Department of Agriculture's plant explorer, David Fairchild, estimated that his Bureau of Plant Introduction had brought into the country nearly 200,000 kinds of plants from all over the world. Nowadays, plant introducers are more cautious than they once were, but they are still at it. They argue that every harmful mistake like the wild hyacinth is balanced by a dozen successes like corn, wheat and apples.

CHAPTER SIXTEEN

The Ones That Went the Other Way

THE adventures of some of our hemisphere's most notable emigrants already have been recounted—those of the potato, the tomato and the turkey. New World tobacco also has been grown in many parts of the Old World since the seventeenth century, and the Kansas sunflower is a leading crop of southeastern Europe. But perhaps the potato's chief rival in importance among New World emigrants is a plant few temperate zone dwellers ever hear of. Formally known as *Manihot esculenta,* it seems to have originated in the Brazilian jungle. Its starchy, rather tasteless root, known by many different popular names such as manioc, cassava, yuca and mandioca, is the chief food—sometimes the sole food— of millions of tropical-zone dwellers all around the world.

Millions of tons are produced annually, but about the only form in which any of it reaches temperate-zone dinner-tables is as tapioca.

Corn, too, has been an important emigrant, though it took much of the world a long time to realize its value. Columbus carried samples to Spain on his first trip back, and these or later shipments got planted, but only as curiosities. Apparently the first Old World region to take more than cursory interest in the grain was Africa. The Elizabethan historian of exploration, Samuel Purchas, quoted a traveler in Africa who had seen corn growing in a Portuguese colony there in 1588 but who remarked: "They make no account of it, for they give it to their hogs."

The traveler was hasty with his no-account. Corn's great virtue is as a livestock feed. About eighty-five percent of the crop in this country usually goes to hogs, cattle and chickens, and our enormous corn harvests are among the chief reasons for our plenitude of meat. In the last half century the rest of the world has come to understand this, with the result that corn acreages have been increasing everywhere.

The most welcome of all the animal emigrants that have gone forth from North America in recent centuries may be a little minnow, *Cambusia affinis,* with an insatiable appetite for the larvae of *Anopheles* mosquitoes, the kind that carry malaria. A native of Florida, this fish has in many places proved far more effective than insecticides or any other measures in keeping down the numbers of those mosquitoes. Public health authorities have given it enthusiastic help in spreading around the globe, and it now may be the most widely distributed of all fresh-water fish.

Our grape vines have had two widely differing types of reception abroad. When they first were taken to France for experimental plant-breeding purposes a century ago, there went with them a nearly invisible louse which lives on their roots. The American grapes had evolved along with the louse, and it does them little harm. The European grape was not so tolerant. Within a few years it seemed likely that the emigrant lice might wipe out most of the vineyards of Europe.

As soon as they realized what was happening, French vineyard owners tried grafting their vines on American grape rootstocks. The stratagem worked almost perfectly. Now most European grapes are grown on American roots, and the destroyers have become the saviors.

The reception given emigrant American muskrats (*Ondatra zibethicus*) in Europe also has been varied. The animals got their start abroad when an Austro-Hungarian landowner took five of them home to his estate in Bohemia in 1905. Some of their descendants escaped on their own, and others so impressed visiting landowners from other parts of Europe that these bought or begged pairs to take home. Now muskrats in the millions live throughout Europe and much of Asia, from France to eastern Siberia and from Finland to northern Iran. In many areas they are warmly welcomed for the fur they produce, but in others they are fought with every available weapon because of the damage they do to stream banks and native wildlife. The Finnish and Russian governments, for instance, have helped the animals to spread around in their domains, but the British government has spent thousands of pounds on a campaign to eradicate them from England and Scotland.

North American white-tailed deer (*Odocoileus virginianus*) and gray squirrels (*Sciurus carolinensis*) have been similarly unpopular emigrants in some places. A number of the deer were turned loose in New Zealand along with red

deer from Europe and other similar game animals in the hope that they would provide good hunting. Now the New Zealand government provides free ammunition to anyone who will shoot them and keeps several hired hunters in the field the year around. In South Africa our gray squirrel astonished and horrified its sponsors by passing up the local oaks and acorns in favor of fruit orchards, where it has debudded and girdled thousands of trees.

The most unwelcome of all our emigrants, however, has been a little beetle (*Leptinotarsa decemlineata*) with bright yellow and black stripes down its back. When first noticed early in the last century, it was a rather rare species, apparently confined to the eastern slopes of the Rockies and to a diet of the leaves of such weeds as the beaked nightshade. Unfortunately, white potatoes belong to the nightshade family. The first taste of the leaves of potato plants set out by settlers persuaded the bugs to abandon the weeds, and the location of their first enthusiastic attack on potatoes in the early 1860's won them the popular name, Colorado potato bug. The nutritious new diet fed a population explosion among the beetles; by 1865 the first hordes had reached Illinois, and by 1874 others were on the Atlantic coast and seeking new frontiers.

Their first foray into Europe was in 1877, when a small number were found in Belgium. That advance party was wiped out. For half a century stringent measures similarly destroyed all other beetle beachheads. World War I weakened the defenses, however, and gave the creatures a foothold in France. They slowly fought their way eastward against desperate resistance. Because of the great importance of the potato crop in eastern Europe, the beetles' invasion of Poland and Russia after World War II led to what may well have been quite sincere, though rather hysterical,

charges that the United States was waging underhanded biological warfare.

A more helpful emigrant is the sweet potato (*Ipomoea batatas*), which was domesticated in South and Central America far back in prehistoric times. About a century ago scientists studying Polynesia, the vast triangular area of the Pacific lying between New Zealand, Hawaii and Easter Island, discovered that the Polynesians also had been raising sweet potatoes since long before Columbus. In addition, these investigators found that the sweet potato was known in Polynesia by names similar to those it has in Peru and neighboring parts of South America.

About four thousand miles of open ocean lie between the easternmost sizeable group of Polynesian islands and the west coast of South America, twice the distance across the Atlantic from Newfoundland to Ireland. It seemed to nineteenth-century anthropologists quite obvious that primitive men could not have crossed such a vast expanse in their canoes. Therefore, the theory went, the islands must have been settled by immigrants from the other direction, most likely from Indonesia or Malaya. And therefore, the fact that both Polynesians and Peruvian Indians raised sweet potatoes and called them by the same name had to be explained either as coincidence or in some other roundabout way.

In the 1930's a young Norwegian ethnologist, Thor Heyerdahl, did a year's research in Polynesia and came to the conclusion that the original settlers of the islands might have reached them from Peru on balsa wood rafts. The strong current and steady easterly trade wind from Peru to the islands, he felt sure, could make even a four-thousand-mile raft voyage feasible. On April 28, 1947, he and five friends set off from the coast of Peru aboard a balsa raft they had

named the *Kon-Tiki*. On August 7 they landed on the island of Raroia, five thousand miles to the west, with several hundred pounds of cargo, including sweet potatoes.

After publication of his best-selling book about the trip, *Kon-Tiki: Across the Pacific by Raft*, Heyerdahl wrote a scholarly work, *American Indians in the Pacific*, presenting the huge assemblage of evidence he had collected from many fields to back his idea. In combination with the *Kon-Tiki* voyage it makes quite plausible the possibility that men and sweet potatoes could have emigrated from Peru to Polynesia, and that along with them there may have gone a few other species, such as certain gourds, wild cotton, pineapples, papaya and other plants. The one important animal, other than *Homo sapiens*, may have been the dog, which was popular in Peru and present on many Polynesian islands long before the arrival of the first European explorers.

So far, however, this kind of emigration can be considered only a possibility. Geographers, anthropologists, botanists and other specialists interested in the subject are in sharp, and sometimes quite unscientifically acrimonious, disagreement. It may be many years before a consensus of expert opinion can be reached.

Another even more startling possibility of pre-historic contacts between widely separated parts of the world involves certain peanuts (*Arachis hypogaea*) and squashes of the genus *Cucurbita* grown in this hemisphere long before Columbus. Primitive varieties of both have been found growing in remote parts of southeastern Asia. They may have been taken there from America by early Spanish and Portuguese explorers of the Pacific, but it also is possible that they reached there centuries earlier via routes not yet known. Specialists in geobotany, the distribution of plants, are at work on the problem.

CHAPTER SEVENTEEN

A Biological Exclusion Act?

THE immigrants and emigrants described thus far are the most noteworthy, but they make up only a small fraction of the total number. Merely to list the names of all species of plants and animals that have entered this country since, say, 1492 A.D., would take several thick volumes. As mentioned earlier, the U.S. Department of Agriculture has brought in some 200,000 species and varieties of plants, and collectors for zoos, circuses and museums have brought in uncounted thousands of kinds of mammals, birds, reptiles, amphibians and other animals.

To be sure, except for plants crossbred with native relatives, nearly all of these have been kept in botanical and zoological gardens, so they have had little influence. Important new immigrants still turn up, however, the most so being disease agents such as the already described Asian flu virus of 1957. But larger creatures of at least some potential influence also still make their ways here occasionally.

In the spring of 1952 a Florida photographer trying to get pictures of a cattle herd near Lake Okeechobee noticed among the cows several birds he thought must be small herons. They had mostly white feathers and bright yellow bills and legs, and they were following the cows to eat the grasshoppers and other insects the grazing animals stirred up. For no special reason the photographer snapped a few pictures of the birds. Several weeks later he happened to meet a bird specialist and showed him the photographs, asking what kind of birds they were. The specialist was astonished. He thought he was acquainted with all the birds ever seen in Florida, but he never had seen these.

It took him some time to find out what they were. When he finally succeeded, his astonishment was greater than before. They were Old World cattle egrets (*Bubulcus ibis*), thousands of miles from what was supposed to be their home.

Eventually, students of bird life found other members of this species scattered southward across the Caribbean islands all the way to Dutch Guiana in the northeastern corner of South America. The best guess about how the birds reached this hemisphere is that a flock must have been helped across the 2000-odd miles of the Atlantic from Africa to the neighborhood of the Guianas by a great easterly gale. But no matter how they got here, they clearly like it here. In the years since the Florida photographer took his pictures, the birds have multiplied rapidly and have spread all the way north to Nova Scotia and west to Texas. At last report they numbered at least 20,000 on this continent, perhaps many more.

Some biologists and naturalists find this alarming. In recent years it has become scientifically fashionable to argue that the arrival of a new species in any habitat is almost certain to have an undesirable effect on that habitat's balance of nature. One group of naturalists has suggested an international board of scientists empowered to regulate—or, better, to prevent—intercontinental movements of species. Many others quite vehemently insist that, at the very least, this country ought to erect impregnable barriers against the entry of new species.

There is no disagreement about the desirability of controlling intercontinental migration of some species, though one of the most obvious cases involves a native animal which we ought to be doing everything possible to keep at home. This is a mosquito named *Aedes aegypti*. At the turn of the century Carlos Finlay, Walter Reed, William Gorgas and other heroes of modern medicine were able to stamp out yellow fever epidemics in this country and many parts of Latin America by showing that it was this mosquito which infected humans with the fever virus and by organizing large-scale campaigns to wipe out the insects' breeding colonies. These efforts were so effective that for several decades it seemed that yellow fever, which in the nineteenth century repeatedly ravaged scores of American cities from Boston to Buenos Aires, had been completely and finally defeated. Now it is known that several kinds of South American monkeys are, in effect, living reservoirs of the virus and that new epidemics are quite feasible if *Aedes aegypti* and the monkey virus get together.

To prevent such catastrophe, Latin America has battled the mosquito unrelentingly and has kept it nearly exterminated south of our border. In its favorite part of the United States, however, the area stretching from North Carolina to Texas, it was ignored for several decades because there were no monkey reservoirs around. The result was an enormous growth in the aegypti mosquito population of that area.

In this country we are accustomed to the idea that our public health standards are among the world's highest. Here is a case where we lag far behind the countries to our south. The Pan American Sanitary Bureau began pleading with our government to do something about the mosquitoes in 1947. Not until 1963 did the United States Congress appropriate funds to start an eradication program, and by the fall of 1964 this program was just entering the stage of preliminary study of the problem.

If it is this difficult to arrange international cooperation in control of so dangerous a species as *Aedes aegypti,* it clearly is not likely that strict regulation of the movements of more amiable creatures will be possible soon. Fortunately, there is room for doubt of the reasoning behind the calls for rigid control of all migrants, especially the idea that any new species is likely to upset the balance of nature. This is based on the assumption that that balance is comparatively stable and quiet. Actually, it is in constant movement.

Many factors are involved in the movement. A basic one is the tendency of nearly all species to produce far more offspring than can survive under most conditions. When conditions improve, a larger number of the young survive and produce more offspring of their own, so that the species' numbers climb rapidly. This, in turn, improves conditions for other species that live on the first one. But when the numbers of these latter increase, they kill and eat more of the former, so that its numbers begin to decline.

This is a highly simplified example of one of the kinds of changes incessantly going on in the relations between different species. One of the world's leading students of these relations is the British ecologist, Charles S. Elton, who also is an authority on international movements of animals and plants. Among his chief interests is the explanation of the sudden rapid increases in the numbers of one kind of insect or another which have been noticed more and more often lately in many parts of the world.

He got a clue to that explanation in a conversation with forestry officials from some of Britain's tropical colonies. The officials listened politely for some time while Elton expounded his ideas about such insect outbreaks. Finally, one of them remarked that he had never seen such outbreaks in his territory. Neither, to Elton's astonishment, had any of the others.

The explanation, or anyway a substantial part of it, is that tropical forests have so many different species of insects that no one of them ever has a chance to indulge in a population explosion. Each species has many predators, and any increase in its numbers quickly increases its predators' numbers, too.

Conversely, Elton found in the course of his lengthy research, it is in precisely those areas where men have most reduced the number of kinds of different insects and other animals that outbreaks of pests are most likely to happen. In this country, for instance, there is a direct connection between our obliterating or driving away many forms of native wildlife and the great success of such immigrants as rats and starlings.

The way to prevent either native or invading species from

becoming too numerous is by means of what Elton calls the conservation of variety. Instead of spreading around insecticides, weed-killers and other poisons, we should encourage native forms of life. They will then be able not only to keep each other's numbers within reasonable bounds but also will make it extremely difficult for an invading pest species to get a toehold.

Clearly, this approach to the problem will be difficult since it means a great change in our way of dealing with other creatures. It does, however, offer some hope of success in controlling harmful immigration, and there is no chance at all for the proposal that we prevent international movements of animals and plants. For one thing, this would require an impossibly high degree of close and continuous international cooperation. For another, it would mean the slaughter of several billion birds.

These are, of course, our migratory birds. Every year they surge into the country in a great tidal wave of life, some from as far away as the Antarctic. With them come uncountable billions of microorganisms, weed seeds, insects and insect eggs.

To suggest seriously that we try to halt that tide by killing the birds would be insane. The result would be catastrophe, starting with an insect plague of unimaginable proportions, since birds are our allies in insect control. On the other hand, if we keep reducing the numbers of native microorganisms and weeds and insects, we also will keep increasing the likelihood that some of those hitchhiking in with migratory birds will find a vacant niche and get a start here, a start that can result in an explosive increase overnight.

In the long run Elton's proposal for conservation of variety may not seem so difficult to put into effect after all. It may be our only hope of keeping the continent liveable.

BIBLIOGRAPHY

Many readers will want to know more about one aspect or another of the story of the international movements of plants and animals. Here is a list of books and articles which can be helpful.

GENERAL

Carrington, Richard, *The Story of Our Earth*. New York, Harper & Brothers, 1956.
> Good background covering the period from the earth's origin to the rise of *Homo sapiens*.

Elton, Charles S., *The Ecology of Invasions by Animals and Plants*. New York, John Wiley & Sons, 1958.
> Sounds formidable but actually is quite readable and full of original ideas about how and why species migrate.

Howells, William, *Back of History*. New York, Doubleday & Company, 1954.
> About the rise of our species and its spread over the Old World and into the New.

"The Bering Strait Land Bridge," *Scientific American*, January, 1962, Vol. 206.
> About the most recent theories on how the ancestors of the American Indians and other immigrant species reached this hemisphere.

DOMESTICATED ANIMALS

Briggs, Hilton M., *Modern Breeds of Livestock*. New York, The Macmillan Company, 1949.
Detailed history of breeds of cattle, pigs, sheep, goats, horses.

"Cattle," *Scientific American*, June, 1958, Vol. 198.
A brief discussion of the breeds and their origins.

Lorenz, Konrad, *King Solomon's Ring*. New York, Thomas Y. Crowell Company, 1952.
Especially for the chapters on imprinting and on the origin of dogs.

"Origin of the Dog," *Natural History*, February, 1958, Vol. 67.
A view of the subject slightly different from that of Lorenz.

Simpson, George Gaylord, *Horses*. New York, Oxford University Press, 1951.
An exhaustive but readable history of the horse family from eohippus to date.

Zeuner, F. E., *A History of Domesticated Animals*. New York, Harper & Row, 1964.
Not very readable, but it has most of the available information on the subject.

OTHER ANIMALS

Insects, The Yearbook of Agriculture for 1952. Washington, D.C., U.S. Department of Agriculture.
A big collection of papers on various insects including many immigrants.

Pearson, T. Gilbert, Editor (and others), *Birds of America*. New York, Doubleday & Company, 1936.
An encyclopedia with articles on starling, English sparrow, pigeon, pheasant and others.

Zinsser, Hans, *Rats, Lice and History*. Boston, Little, Brown and Company, 1934.
Some of the interesting parts of the story of the long association of rats and man.

MICRO-ORGANISMS

Eberson, Frederick, *Man Against Microbes: The Story of Modern Preventive Medicine.* New York, Ronald Press, 1963.
    Includes some of the stories of many immigrant microbes.

"Micro-organisms, What They Are, Where They Grow, What They Do." Washington, D.C., U.S. Government Printing Office, 1964.
    This pamphlet is an excellent short introduction to the subject.

Rosenberg, Charles E., *The Cholera Years.* Chicago, University of Chicago Press, 1962.
    A study of the cholera epidemics of the last century and the gradual switch from the 1830's view that cholera was punishment for sin to the 1860's view that it had something to do with bad sanitation.

PLANTS

Anderson, Edgar, *Plants, Man and Life.* Boston, Little, Brown and Company, 1951.
    One of the most readable books by a working scientist you ever are likely to find.

Schery, Robert W., *Plants for Man.* New York, Prentice-Hall, Inc., 1952.
    Dull compared with Anderson's book but has some information on immigrant plants he does not cover.

EMIGRANTS

Heyerdahl, Thor, *Kon-Tiki: Across the Pacific by Raft.* New York, Rand McNally & Co., 1950.
    An exciting story of adventure and scientific achievement, although with controversial conclusions.

Index